Praise for Barbara R. Avila's *Seeing Autism*

"*Seeing Autism* is full of strategies to build a better relationship with someone with autism, but it's vastly more. Readers are invited to understand the 'beauty and complexity of autism' and are provided an essential lens to allow us to foster the deep connections all humans need and that allow us to be known. Barb Avila brilliantly challenges current ways of thinking when it comes to autism. She walks us through what we need to know and teaches us how to apply that knowledge in meaningful, fun, and practical ways. An essential read for every parent, teacher, or anyone in relationship with someone with autism."

–Tina Payne Bryson, LCSW, Ph.D.,
New York Times Bestselling co-author of
The Whole-Brain Child and *No-Drama Discipline*,
and author of *The Bottom Line for Baby*

"Barbara Avila is more than a teacher or counselor. She's a connector. In *Seeing Autism: Connection Through Understanding*, Barbara doesn't just explain autism to us; she shows us what it's like to live with autism and how to live in heart-connection with those who are autistic. This book is full of facts and practical advice from the worlds of human development, brain science, and psychology. The information is fascinating and essential. The ideas and suggestions are realistic and practical. But the thing that makes this book truly unique is Barbara's emphasis on the importance of human relationships and the core needs that autistic people have—to be seen and understood. This book is an invaluable guide for anyone who

identifies as autistic, those who believe they may be on the spectrum, and family members or friends of those with autism."
—Pamela Schavaun Scott,
Author, Marriage and Family Therapist, MA, MFT Co-author of the book *Game Addiction: The Experience and the Effect*.

"As a psychiatric professional and single mother of a teen with autism, I want to go out and buy this book for everyone who meets my son! He and I have known Barb since his toddlerhood, and I have done my best to soak up everything I was able to of her ideas and wisdom. Barb's brilliance, loving support, and creative problem-solving have always shined through, imbuing hope where sometimes I feared there might be none. And in *Seeing Autism*, she has packed her knowledge and insight all in one place. You will be inspired, excited, and passionate about trying new ways to connect with your partner/friend/child/co-worker with autism. This book is such a gift. Please enjoy!"
—Diane Solomon, Ph.D., PMHNP-BC CNM
Dynamic, strategic health policy advocate;
behavioral health clinician

"The most balanced, insightful, encouraging, and inspiring book I have read on autism. I can't wait to share its actionable advice with our son, family, friends, and support team. This book is a game changer. Finally, a book that truly understands people with autism and shows us how we can empower them to advocate for themselves at any age and developmental stage."
—Corinna Gilligan,
Mother, Advocate, Business Owner

SEEING AUTISM

Barbara R. Avila, M.S.

SEEING AUTISM

Connection Through Understanding

Synergy autism center

Developmental editing, line editing, proofreading, cover design, and interior
book design provided by Indigo: Editing, Design, and More

Developmental and line editor: Kristen Hall-Geisler
Proofreaders: Cooper Lee Bombardier and Sarah Curin
Cover and interior designer: Olivia Hammerman

www.indigoediting.com

For autistic individuals:
may you be seen for who you are and all the value you
bring to our homes, classrooms, communities,
and workplaces.

"The question is not what you look at, but what you see."
—Henry David Thoreau

Contents

Introduction

What you hold in your hands is a portal into a deep understanding of autism that you may not have known you needed until now. The knowledge I am sharing with you I have learned through research and through the countless people on the autism spectrum who I have had the pleasure to meet.

In my years as an autism specialist, I have met and connected with amazing human beings who process the world differently. I do not speak for them. I stand beside them and encourage their own contributions, as they are necessary for our collective future. I only hope that I can do justice in sharing what I have found to be the best way not to cure autism but to alleviate the social and sensory challenges that seem to stand in the way of people on the spectrum having satisfying and life-long connections with others.

In this book, you will find insight into the autistic mind along with essentials to build relationships. I am not here to convince you of anything. I am here to extend the invitation to get to know autism at a new level. You will learn that it is through *seeing* autism that you can form bonds. We all wish to be truly seen by those we love, who guide us and nourish us. All of my recommendations are based on current neuroscience studies, developmental research, evidence-based practices, discussions with adults on the autism spectrum, and my thirty-plus years of experience. I have been blessed to have befriended, worked with, and guided more people than I can count who have autism or some variation of it. I am uniquely positioned with my advanced degree in early development and my extensive experience with autistics of all ages to bring to you this guide for establishing the foundations of social engagement for those on the autism spectrum. My wish for you is to better understand autism processing so that you, too, can see the beauty of autism within someone you know.

Children who were once in my preschool classroom are now client-friends either in college or working in our community. Since I target building relationships in my work, the age of the individual does not matter. Everyone, from infant to adult, is oriented by nature to build relationships. Some people may be more social than others, but it is a human need to connect with others.

The first person I ever met with autism was an eight-year-old child at a camp where I volunteered as a high school senior. He was full of energy and athleticism. He sprinted across the camp at top speeds, loved to swim, loved the routines of the camp, and communicated through his actions and behaviors. I learned quickly that transitioning a child with autism out of a swimming pool can be quite a chaotic mess of confusion and frustration. Observing and guiding that young boy for that one weekend sparked an incredible curiosity in me to learn more about autism.

It was the late 1980s at this point, and there was not much information about autism yet. I read everything I could get my hands on. I studied neuroscience and child development while working with more and more children and teens with autism. I was struck by the incredible mix of kindness and intellect combined with sensory flooding, severe aggression, and miscommunication. I spent countless long hours at university libraries. As the years progressed, I worked as a line therapist, a group-home parent, an educational assistant, a teacher for both integrated and nonintegrated classrooms, a consultant in schools, a behavior consultant through state resources, a parent coach for those involved with juvenile detention and child welfare, a consultant on legal cases, and a trainer for anyone who wanted to know more about autism. By studying neuroscience, family-based intervention, and behavioral training, I learned that working with families provides a critical foundation for the growing child, teen, or adult with autism. By working with families, I can help secure the early foundations of social and dynamic living. By working with the professionals surrounding a child, there is consistency, trust, and security that creates a nest to prepare that person to fly. When an autistic person is surrounded by people who understand and truly see them, they thrive.

This book is not just another autism book with tips and techniques for fixing or teaching skills to someone with the diagnosis of autism. Please do not treat it as such. I've created this portal to help you connect more deeply with someone you know, adore, or guide. The essentials in this book do not *teach* relationship skills to the individual but allow you to build a relationship with them by having a better understanding of their processing.

As you may already know, or as you will discover, most people with autism intrinsically want to engage—they are just not given the chance in a way that works for them. But while the intrinsic motivation is there, their confidence for relationship building is low. Their ability to trust themselves and be resilient is minimal at best. Navigating the rapidly changing and unpredictable scenarios of relationships with people can be overwhelming. And here's the good news: you can make adjustments to allow and foster deeper bonds for parenting and guiding to bolster friendship and companionship. Your child, partner, or friend can create bonds of friendship and deeper intimacy. They just need you to understand them first.

This Book Is for You

I wrote this book for you! I really did. You are the parents, professionals, friends, neighbors, and coworkers of anyone who has autism. You are the person suspected of being autistic. My aim is that the information you will glean from reading this book will help you better understand and see autism for its beauty and complexity.

Many people are going to pick up this book and assume it is only for parents. But guess what? Some parents are already in tune with a lot of what I present here. They know their child and the moments that things may have changed. They are yearning for this work. So if you are a professional choosing to pick this book up and take it home, I applaud you. You "get it." You know that people with autism need to be respected, understood, and seen. Thank you for being here and being a part of the change to better support people with autism.

- This book is for you if you are the parent who suspects your very young child may have autism. You are seeking a bond and healthy, secure attachment with your child.

Here you will find the basics to ensure you can engage your child more successfully.

- This book is for you if you are the professional who is trying to teach a person with autism independence, advocacy, regulation, social engagement, or even articulation. Here you will find the basics to make any intervention you choose to be more successful.

- This book is for you if you are the partner or spouse of a person diagnosed with autism who longs to love and connect more deeply with them. These essentials will help you understand why some aspects are challenging and guide you to have more fulfilling moments together.

- This book is for you if you are the peer or coworker who wants to understand and connect more on a daily basis with someone with autism. These essentials will guide your understanding and help you ensure a more satisfying working relationship and/or friendship.

- This book is for you if you are the sibling of someone with autism and wish to have a more fulfilling relationship with your sibling. I know you do not want to become their therapist or interventionist. This book will help you better understand your sibling's processing so you can connect more deeply with them.

Is It Autism?

A person can receive the diagnosis of autism at any age. There are two-year-olds diagnosed with autism and there are seventy-five-year-olds diagnosed with autism. Psychologists, doctors, counselors, and other mental health practitioners determine whether someone qualifies. I will be diving into the symptoms of autism in my first chapter, titled "The Cascade Effect."

One of the confusing aspects of autism is that everything you see in autism also happens in typical development. Children with and without autism vary considerably as to when they talk, how they talk, and if they talk. They also vary on how they play with toys and interact with people. For example, we know that some people are shy and others enjoy being the center of attention. For a medical or educational diagnosis, the severity of symptoms must be significant enough to hinder their growth and development. In order to receive the diagnosis of autism, one must have symptoms that affect their social engagement and restrict their interests and behaviors. Again, we may bite our nails or tap our foot when we think and process, but these are not usually considered extreme enough to qualify under autism as they are not significantly hindering our developmental progress or quality of life.

While people can be diagnosed with autism at any age, symptoms of autism must have been identified early in development, as it is considered a "developmental delay." I commonly have teens and adults (and parents) reach out to explore whether they may be on the autism spectrum. It can be quite helpful for teens and adults to recognize that the challenges that they experienced growing up were due to their unique processing rather than something they did wrong. Often within the first few months of working with a family, the parents wonder if they may be on the autism spectrum themselves.

Many adults would rather be referred to as "autistics" rather than "adults with autism." When I first entered the field of autism, everyone used the term "autistics," but when I went into graduate school, I was reprimanded for using "autistics" instead of "children with autism." My original understanding came from the idea is that people with disabilities should be seen as people first rather than as a disabled individual. But many autistics feel that autism defines them, so they want it as a title rather than as an appendage. I have asked many adults which they prefer and find that about half of those I have interviewed prefer "autistic," and the other half do not care or do not choose to disclose their autism at all. I encourage you to simply ask someone's preference and speak with them accordingly.

The Beauty of Autism

Some of the most honest, forthright, intelligent, and funny people I know have autism. I have met individuals who experience classical music or Japanese anime with an intensity and factual knowledge that has given me an appreciation for those topics that I would not have had otherwise. I have met individuals who have knowledge and memory for historical facts that far surpassed my memory from my years in school. Their memories for these facts enrich our conversation in ways I couldn't have imagined. At the same time, I have enjoyed learning from individuals who experience the world differently with their unique sensory systems. I have enjoyed flicking cards back and forth in front of my eyes to share the way the light through the window hit each card. I have participated in drawing detailed road maps with individuals from memory—complete with house numbers—in neighborhoods they have seen just once. I have been in awe many times by the way some people with autism experience the breeze on their face or the sparkle of dust in the sunlight. I think we all have something to learn from those with autism.

Some autistics have what is called synesthesia, which is when someone experiences two or more sensory channels together. Someone may see colors when they hear music or experience another person's emotions as colors. I have been told that I have a warm aura about me that helps me be trustworthy.

I invite you to love, live, and work alongside people with autism. They have amazing ways of seeing the world that will change how you see it too. If you take the time to gaze into the way people with autism see the world, you will gain a new perspective on your own life as well. We need more people in this world who think differently, and we need more people who appreciate those differences. Welcome to the autism community.

How to Use This Book

I suspect you are here because you wish to build, deepen, or strengthen a relationship with someone with autism in your classroom, clinic, or in your own home. But you may be wondering what this book will do for you. What will it do for you if you are new to autism and have an eighteen-month-old? What will this book do for you if you have had years of misunderstanding yourself or your child? What if you're wondering if it may have been autism all along?

The pages that lie ahead hold the keys to seeing and understanding autism. With these keys of understanding, you will then be equipped to create situations and environments that are ideally suited for a person you know with autism or for yourself. Understanding and valuing how someone processes information provides the path for creating connections. You cannot step into the world of autism for yourself, your child, your client, or your loved one wielding tools, strategies, and scripts in the hopes that one will do the trick to fix the autism or the behaviors that challenge you. With an approach to fix, you give the person the message that there is something wrong with them. And who would feel compelled to connect with someone who wants to fix you?

I will certainly and happily share themes, topics, strategies, and tools that will support you. But be sure to seek understanding first. Then and only then can you apply tools and strategies so that they make sense for that individual.

I am not here to fix autism. Most adults on the autism spectrum do not wish to fix or cure their autism but do wish to alleviate the challenges in processing social and sensory information. As you will see, through understanding the developmental underpinnings of these, we can connect more effectively with those with autism.

It can be very challenging for families and professionals to grapple with our current societal mindset to fix or cure disorders and differences. Society drives us to take action and strive for "normality." Autism may be challenging to that very thinking. Autistic individuals are not broken. They process differently. And just like all humans, they do need to be supported and guided with love, respect, and understanding—rather than being fixed just to "fit in." I am saddened, for example, at how many interventions for people with autism focus on teaching behaviors to meet norms without consideration of developmental foundations. Well-meaning professionals offer strategies, scripts, and other band-aids to help children "fit in." They pay very little attention to helping these children learn the independence and confidence to manage the deluge of social and sensory information coming at them. In current interventions, we tend to offer temporary solutions rather than long-term, developmental, and relationship-based support.

Some of you may be thinking that I am only speaking of and providing guidance to those people with autism who do not display severely challenging behaviors, are quite verbal, and who do not seem considerably impacted. Please note: I am not only speaking here to those in our communities that have learned to mask or camouflage their autism. I am talking about the full range of autism. And to support rather than fix to provide the dignity for those people who may be unable to communicate in ways we readily understand.

"Camouflaging" or "masking" are terms used by people with autism who try to hide their sensory sensitivities, repetitive movements, or other behaviors just to "fit in." It can also lead to what is known as "autistic burnout," which happens when one has masked for a very long time and feels utterly and totally exhausted by it.

If You Like Analogies...

Some people like to use analogies and metaphors, while others find them confusing and obtuse. I offer one here, but please jump ahead if you do not find them helpful. Here goes.

Teaching someone to fit in may be akin to our building bridges to connect with those we love with autism. In the summer, we may build a lovely bridge of accommodations across a stream when the water is at its lowest and the weather is at its best. The bridge works perfectly for that one season and as long as the weather holds. However, the bridge was not built to withstand the water rising, and that water will soon crash into and over that bridge. The bridge will eventually crumble under the stress of the stream that becomes that river. The bridge that was built to help the person meet and engage with peers on the other side of the bridge is lost or damaged.

Without that bridge or temporary support, isolation for that individual is inevitable. They may have occasional days or even weeks when the stream will allow their crossing. Or they may give up hope of ever crossing again if the bridge has gotten so many winter beatings that it is no longer usable or reliable.

If we consider and predict the ebb and flow of the water, we can better connect the two sides of the stream. We can build a more substantial and higher bridge. We can redirect the water or even build a boat. By understanding and respecting the flow of water, we support better long-term solutions rather than simply trying to build temporary fixes that will inevitably break under pressure.

As you may already see, my aim here is not necessarily to fix the bridge or to make the person forge the stream when it turns into a river. Either of these could lead to devastating blows to one's self-esteem when they fail. I want to give you the knowledge so that you can navigate to the child or person with autism on their side of the river. With the information in this book, you will be able to join them on their shore and enjoy the scenery from their point of view. You may have a child with autism who learns that boating is amazing and wishes to learn how to sail with you. And you may have a partner who has built a life on that other shore and is no longer open to routine crossings of that river. They may choose to forge the river occasionally and only when absolutely necessary—but they love to have company in small doses. You may have the architect in your life who has great ideas about building that substantial bridge. And you may have the child who tentatively and carefully learns how to build better bridges for themselves while also dabbling in learning to sail.

I would be seriously remiss if I relied on my own processing or that of non-autistic clinicians, authors, and researchers in the writing of this book. Therefore I rely, trust, and honor the myriad autistics I have met to share their experiences in helping us understand their processing. I am sure that what I have to offer you will not always exactly match your baby, toddler, child, teen, young adult, partner, sibling, or friend. Each person has their own personality, their own preferences, and their own temperament, just like any of us. There is no one book that will guide us exactly on what to do at all times.

The way I see it, I know autism, and you know an autistic person. My goal is for you to truly understand the underpinnings of why people with autism act the way they do and how they process information differently. In this book, I share research combined with my experiences and recommendations so you can join someone with autism in ways that will feel welcoming and productive.

If You Are New to the Diagnosis

Some of you may be new to the diagnosis of autism. You wonder if this book is for you. You may be in the early stages of understanding what it means to have autism. It warms my heart to know that you may be reading this to avoid trying to fix autism and to better understand it. My mission with this book is for you to appreciate the autistic experience so that you, too, can benefit from your child's, partner's, or friend's perspective while parenting, befriending, or guiding them.

And if you yourself have been diagnosed with autism recently, I welcome you. I hope that you will find this book helpful for understanding your own processing while helping you define what you need or want for yourself. I know you want connection and love in your life. My goal is that this book gives you hope and a path forward. If you do find that it speaks to your processing, please share it with someone you love or someone who wants to connect with you.

A Special Note for Parents

I want you to know that I see you. You want love and connection for your child with autism now and in the future. You want them to feel loved, valued, and celebrated. You want them to be as successful as they can be as individuals with love in their hearts. And we know from research that having healthy, secure, and engaged relationships early in life with our primary caregivers predicts later health and well-being. The chapters that lie ahead will help you join your autistic child of any age—with more knowledge, confidence, and joy. Social connections throughout life stave off depression and extends our lives. *Seeing Autism* will help you join your child, teen, or adult so that they feel seen and understood without compromising your own well-being. Our shared goal for your child is increased self-confidence and flexibility. For when we all feel seen, understood, heard, and validated, we all thrive.

And If You Think You've Read It All

Even if you are reading this long after an initial diagnosis and you think you've read everything on the subject, my unique stance will be refreshing and new for you. And please, when you read this book, do not beat yourself up if you find yourself wishing you had known these essentials earlier. Our brains are equipped to learn at any age. Center yourself to understand, connect, and practice what you learn in this book. Use the reflections at the end of each section to drive your understanding further. Forgive yourself and start this new chapter with yourself, your child, partner, or friend with acceptance and engagement.

The Flow of the Book:
UNDERSTAND → CONNECT → PRACTICE

I have written this book over several years of my work with individuals, families, and community members. The order in which I present information here is very important. You will find that I have split it up into three parts. At the end of each part, I offer you a page for reflecting on how that section may have changed or deepened how you see autism.

In the first section, Part 1, I guide you to understand the research in the early indicators of autism and how those have a cascade effect leading to the behaviors we see. I take you on the journey of understanding the experience of the sensory and emotional flood and how your own self-care and well-being can either add to or reduce that flood. In the next section, Part 2, I guide you to prepare an environment for optimal connection with someone with autism. You will learn how to create interactions that make sense and feel safe for those on the autism spectrum. And last but not least, in Part 3, I provide guidance for practicing the core muscle that needs strengthening in autism: social reciprocity. I give you the understanding and ideas for bringing practice into your daily routines together as well as sharing a few things that may not quite go as planned and what to do in those cases.

I have also designed the book so that you can jump to aspects that make the most sense for you at the time you pick up the book. For example, if you are not interested in what early infant studies are telling us about autism, you can skip the first chapter on "The Cascade Effect." And if you are wanting idea lists to get your own creative juices flowing for practicing in everyday life, you can jump to appendix 6 for ideas.

However you choose to read and digest this book, I am happy you are here. My wish is for deep and fulfilling relationships for those on the autism spectrum throughout their lives. I hope this book helps even just a smidge toward that goal. Every step of progress matters.

PART I

UNDERSTAND

It is through understanding that we find clarity.
It is through understanding that we find calm.

CHAPTER 1

The Cascade Effect

*"Takiwātanga" is the Maori word for autism
and means "in their own time and space."*

In this first chapter, we dive deep into the symptoms of autism as we are coming to understand them through research studies. At this moment, you might not be particularly interested in the research behind the recommendations I share in this book, so please feel free to skip ahead. You can always return to this chapter as a reference.

Research studies in autism and child development provide the foundations for my work in helping people establish quality connections with one another. The research in autism can give us a clear picture of what we have offered autistic individuals thus far, while the research in child development gives us an understanding of how children with many different types of learning differences grow into adulthood.

The Core Symptoms of Autism

I'd like to start with what I think is a bit of a shocker. The most common interventions specific to autism rarely start by addressing the core symptoms. Yes, you read that right. Children and adults with the diagnosis of autism demonstrate difficulty with social reciprocity and exhibit restricted or repetitive interests, but the immediate response by professionals (and insurance companies) is to recommend behavioral and speech therapy—stat! Don't get me wrong. Of course we want children to be compliant and use words to tell us their wants and needs. Keep in mind that developmentally, these are both downstream from the requisite foundations. It is when a child is actively engaged in interactions with caregivers that they learn to use words and to expand their play. Before getting too much into this tragic issue with our current state of interventions, let's first explore the current definition of autism.

A diagnosis of autism is not determined by any blood, genetic, or other type of test. The diagnosis is made through observation of the behaviors or symptoms that someone exhibits. At this time, we know that autism has a genetic component, but it is not clear what that is—yet. There are also a lot of theories about what causes autism, but as of the writing of this book, nothing definitive has been identified. In fact, it seems possible that we may never find just one specific cause, as autism is a cluster of behaviors that interfere with the processing of social information resulting in what is considered "autism."

The Diagnostic and Statistical Manual (DSM) is published and updated by the American Psychiatric Association and describes a variety of mental health diagnoses we experience as humans. The fifth edition of the DSM was published in 2013.

People receive diagnoses, which then drive their treatment plans. One of those diagnoses is Autism Spectrum Disorder. Prior to 2013, there was also a diagnosis of Asperger's Syndrome, which is still used by many in conversation but is no longer included in the DSM-5 nor used in medical practice.

Adults on the autism spectrum object to describing autism as "high functioning" versus "low functioning." It is thought that people who would be considered "high functioning" may be masking their more severe symptoms and are struggling more than they may outwardly appear. Conversely, people who may be considered "low functioning" may be much more aware and engaged than they appear.

To receive an autism diagnosis, a person must exhibit two distinct categories of behavior, having displayed at least some of these behaviors since early childhood: (1) Difficulties with social reciprocity; and (2) Restricted or repetitive interests or behaviors. The person then receives a severity rating based on their symptoms. A level 1 diagnosis is made when the behaviors or symptoms seem to be less impactful to the individual than level 2, where they are considered to be more severely impactful to the individual's well-being and development.

Social Reciprocity

As humans, we are born helpless, but we have the budding ability to engage with our primary caregivers so they can provide for our safety and well-being. We learn to gain their attention when we need something, and they in turn learn to read our cues, cries, and discomfort. This early dance between parent and child is the basis for what is called "social reciprocity." It starts soon after birth, and if both the environment and child's system are ready and nurtured, the seed of social reciprocity will develop with its own unique and healthy complexity. As a child grows, this early social reciprocity adds elements and layers quickly. The child soon learns to engage with others beyond their primary caregivers while also learning to incorporate objects into their interactions.

As a clinician, I often look to infant studies to better understand the roots of what I see in the behavior of my clients with autism. I strongly believe that if we better understand the natural progression of development combined with the autistic experience, we can better support and guide connections.

Infants develop social reciprocity well before they are able to speak words. We gaze at our caregivers when we are hungry, cold, or tired. We smile, and our caregivers smile back. Later, we engage in social reciprocity in the form of peekaboo. This playful game of back-and-forth engagement often has facial expressions and gestures in the mix, and maybe even sound effects, but not usually any words from the child yet. As adults, we often add words, but we are not expecting a full understanding or use of words from the child until later. As infants we look to our caregivers for food, love, and comfort well before we have the words to request, comment, and engage. Keep this fact in mind as we explore the cascade effect these early social reciprocity moments have on a child's development and why targeting them is key.

"Social reciprocity" is a fancy way of describing the back-and-forth "dance" we engage in from the moment we introduce ourselves through to saying our vows in marriage or celebrating ten years as a member of an employee team. The dance requires each person to initiate and respond with contingent actions tied to what the other said or did. Whenever we are talking, sharing, dancing, playing, or laughing with someone else, we are engaging in social reciprocity. The term "reciprocal" means that both parties are actively participating and that their responses are dependent on the other's actions.

I like to think of social reciprocity as also having a rhythm to it. The rhythm of the back-and-forth can detract from or add to your connection with others. We may initiate with someone (which I and many psychologists call offering a "bid for connection"), and they either do not respond or they respond in a way that feels awkward or disconnected. Similarly, we may offer a bid for connection, and the other person responds in a way that feels well-timed and connected so that we feel seen and heard. Harvard's Center on the Developing Child calls this the "serve and return" between infants and their caregivers. You can imagine a tennis or ping-pong ball being served back and forth across the court or table. If the receiver consistently misses the ball, either the game is over or the server must adjust how they are serving the ball. Just as in tennis, it is a delicate balance; you want to be challenged but not overly compensated for, either. Not only are we attracted to people with whom we feel "in sync," there is now proof that it helps us feel closer and more connected. Research shows that we offer our assistance more often to those with whom we have been in sync, even as toddlers.

One 2020 infant study showed that infants who were bounced on their caregiver's lap near a researcher who also bounced in synchrony with them were more likely to later demonstrate prosocial behavior with that researcher. Following the synchronous bouncing, they were more likely to help the researcher access something out of reach or that they had dropped (Cuadros, et al. 2020).

Throughout this book, when I discuss "early social reciprocity," I am referring to the beautiful, simple, playful, and sweet feedback loop between infant and caregiver. Early social reciprocity is often observed when a caregiver is holding their baby in their lap in a face-to-face, relaxed posture. Parents and children coo and gaze back and forth. They smile at one another, each making each other's smile a little bit bigger. It is the back and forth laughter like when your baby or toddler laughs and it makes you laugh even more.

Joint Attention

Once social reciprocity is established, infants start to notice the world around them in addition to their caregivers. We start bringing objects to our mouths, and into our play and exploration. This new exploration also gives way to what is called "joint attention." Joint attention is an expansion of social reciprocity. At the basic level, joint attention describes the action of two people gazing together at the same object—jointly attending to it.

We develop the basics of social reciprocity and joint attention early in life. We continue to use their increasingly complex forms to build relationships throughout our lives. When we talk to a friend about a topic, share ideas and insights, or work on problems together, we are using our social reciprocity and subsequent joint attention skills.

In the first few years of life, joint attention is essential for learning language. Our caregivers notice that we are gazing at an object, toy, or even a pet that they then name for us. Later, we may begin to point to things, vocalize, and look to our caregiver with the expectation that they will label it for us. By following someone's gaze, we also learn how others feel and think about things. In fact, joint attention can even keep us alive. If a person notices something dangerous and we follow their gaze to learn of some impending danger, we can flee to safety. Following someone's gaze to an object of interest and back again helps us discover new interests, likes, and dislikes through the eyes of others we trust.

As a person grows and forms relationships, they continually use this complex facial gazing, social reciprocity, and joint attention to communicate with others. Two people who have known each other for many years may be able to look across a crowded room to each other and communicate silently about a topic using only their facial expressions, gaze, and gestures. Good friends may gaze at one another and start laughing about a previous encounter they both remember without having to say a word. We may use a simple comforting gaze to indicate our love or care for others. All of these interactions are rooted in the early development of social reciprocity and joint attention.

There is one video that went viral on social media in 2020 that demonstrates social reciprocity and joint attention beautifully. In the video, a father figure and an infant are sitting side by side on a couch. They are watching a show together, and they each take turns "commenting" on the show. The baby is making sounds and gazing with exaggerated gestures. They do not seem to have any words yet. The father-figure is responding exuberantly with "I know, right?" and waiting for the baby's next "comment." The baby gestures and vocalizes at the TV, then to the father. The father then answers, "Really! Is that so?" and looks to the baby again. The back-and-forth feedback loop between them is adorable, but it also demonstrates the early social reciprocity and joint attention that happens well before a child's first words. It is through these increasingly complex interactions that we find friendship, learn to collaborate with others, and find our sense of belonging and community.

The Cascade Effect

There are countless factors and variables at play helping our seeds of social engagement germinate and flourish throughout our lives. We may be in loving, caring homes that nurture the seeds of social reciprocity and joint attention. Or we may be in abusive homes that stunt or delay the seeds early in development. Just as easily, we may be in the idyllic environment for seeds to grow but our seeds themselves are not yet ready. They may need to gain strength and wellness within their own biological systems before sprouting into the world. Infants who later develop autism are born with the innate drive to socially connect just like everyone else. It is the developmental step from early, quiet, and simple social reciprocity to the complexity of joint attention that may not occur in the same manner—delaying language and social development.

Autistic adults commonly report experiencing sensory input differently. The young child may be experiencing an internal landscape, making sensory experiences more vivid and potentially more overwhelming than the rest of us.

Again, "social reciprocity" is a diagnostic phrase used to refer to the back-and-forth mutual exchange between people. Social reciprocity starts early in development. A caregiver gazes at a baby, the baby looks back, and the two continue in a connected and fluid manner. The eye contact you might witness in this infant-caregiver relationship may be fleeting, but it also may be sustained. The infant may gaze at the caregiver, then look away, then look back again to the caregiver.

Early infant research on social reciprocity guides us to understand how it supports later healthy development as well as how disruptions in this early stage can cause challenges later. For example, psychologists found that if a parent "chases" their infant's gaze rather than allowing the infant to shift away and come back on their own, the child may get overstimulated and struggle with their own overall ability to calm themselves. In the 1960s and 1970s, child development researchers Mary Ainsworth and John Bowlby helped the child development world understand the importance of early attachment with caregivers. The research has been primarily focused on the effects on the child when their caregiver is challenged by such mental health needs as depression or anxiety. Bowlby shared that "the early attachment experience creates internal working models—lifelong templates for preconceptions of the value and reliability of relationships, close and otherwise" (Rees 2007). The baby develops templates for their later social interactions in childhood, teen years, and even into adult life.

It is only recently that we have seen research in early engagements where the child has sensory or regulation challenges within their own neurobiological system that impact their readiness for that early social engagement. If the child were struggling neurobiologically, well-intentioned caregivers would react accordingly in a loving and supportive manner. They would attempt to decrease engagement to ensure the child's well-being by reducing overall stimulation. With this shift to decrease stimulation, you would also see decreased engagement in early back-and-forth social reciprocity. Subsequently you would see a drop in the sheer number of engagement opportunities for the child to learn. Therefore we see the cascade effect starting with the inner state of the child's system, which then impacts the early social reciprocity between child and caregiver, which gives way to joint attention with increasing levels of complexity. This cascade effect leads to the behaviors we call "autism."

Natural Human Differences

We are all driven to connect with others in our lives. Some of us are considered extroverts, thriving on numerous social connections in our lives—getting energy from the time we spend with others. And some of us are introverts, needing time alone to refuel our personal energy sources. I repeat: we are all driven to connect. Some of us are social butterflies in school and on the playground. Others of us become more social as we age, finding our people after years of being shy and withdrawn. We may thrive with just a few close friends. And still others of us realize early on that we enjoy deeper connections with just a few special people rather than a gaggle of friends and acquaintances. Just because someone has autism does not mean they are unmotivated or incapable of socially engaging. In fact, it doesn't even dictate whether they are introverts or extroverts. I have known many extroverted autistics who love being around others and make plenty of eye contact.

Why Care about Early Development?

Learning what foundational and developmental building blocks need to be in place for us to be fully social human beings helps us understand how to support those who may struggle. There are so many neurological connections being made in our infancy that set the stage for how we interact with the world as adults.

When humans are born, as I mentioned, we are still very much dependent on our primary caregivers for sustenance and safety. Through research in this early part of our development, we know that a staggering number of neuronal connections are made based on both our internal and external experiences. There is extensive research on the effects of interaction styles with infants and how those interaction styles create either healthy or unhealthy attachments with primary care providers. These attachment styles guide us into future relationships.

There is a famous study called the Still Face Experiment by Dr. Edward Tronick. His research from the 1970s helped us understand the dramatic effects on a child when a caregiver is depressed or unavailable. Tronick demonstrated infant distress when the caregiver was unavailable momentarily. Simply by having the caregiver break their gaze and become unresponsive for a very short period of time, infants became significantly distressed. During this experiment, an infant playfully engaged in a back-and-forth with their primary caregiver. Then the caregiver would deliberately switch to a "still face," one that lacks emotion, for a full two minutes. If you are curious, you can find this study and video easily on the internet. The experiment is disconcerting to watch, but it is stunning to see how much the caregiver's affect can alter the baby's well-being. The baby becomes agitated with the failed attempts to engage their caregiver. Imagine if the infant, from a neurobiological standpoint, was distressed. A difference in sensory processing or even a simple time delay in gaze shifting could have an incredible impact on the back-and-forth social reciprocity between caregiver and child. The child's trajectory of development would be altered and potentially headed in a different direction.

We know from infant studies that most infants who later develop autism do engage in the early back-and-forth gazing with their caregivers. However, many parents have said that they noticed slight differences in those early engagements, especially if they have older children as reference points for development. What is noted in the research is that it is not until between a child's first and second birthday that we begin to see the symptoms that qualify for an autism diagnosis. And by the time that an autism diagnosis is made, there has been a cascade effect from that very early and basic social reciprocity.

According to the CDC, 1 in 54 children has been diagnosed with autism spectrum disorder with the average diagnosis being made around a child's third birthday. There is so much that we can do to guide and support before a child is technically diagnosed, when we first suspect things are changing course.

Time Delay in Shifting Attention

Infant studies have been instrumental in helping us determine the early indicators of autism. The infants in the studies are often siblings of children who have developed autism, as the siblings have a greater risk of developing autism themselves.

I find it fascinating that several studies have demonstrated that infants who later develop autism have an attention-shifting time delay. They take longer to disengage from one stimulus (e.g., a light) to then shift to a new stimulus (Franchini et al. 2019). There are also infant studies that demonstrate that the infants who later develop autism do not shift their attention as readily to social stimulus (that is, faces) as infants who do not develop autism (Shultz, Klin, and Jones 2018).

Take a moment to imagine a caregiver smiling at their child while holding a stuffed bear. The infant looks to the adult, then to the bear; now imagine that it takes more time than expected to shift the infant's attention. The caregiver may say "bear," but the child is still looking at the adult or is mid-shift when the word is provided. The adult then moves on quickly to label the bottle he has waiting for the infant. By the time the baby's attention has shifted to the bottle, both the words "bear" and "bottle" have floated by seemingly without being connected with anything specific. The synchronization of words and interactions continues to be off kilter. The sheer potential for confusion and overwhelm for infants with delayed shifting of attention early in development seems staggering.

With knowledge of this time delay causing rifts in language development and social engagement, we are one step closer to knowing how to help. In chapter 6, I will discuss in depth how to give infants, children, teens, and adults more time to process the information around them, especially social information.

Current and ongoing research through the Kennedy Krieger Institute, for example, suggests motor deficits in those with autism. This would make speech production and attention shifting difficult, resulting in some of the challenges you see in autism. For example, when a person repeats a phrase over and over again, it may be that they intend to say something, and their motor centers go on autopilot, making them say or do things that seem repetitive—what I call "static loops." If a child from a very early age has difficulty in making their body do what they want it to do, the implications are again staggering for the mismatch of attention and experiences.

Supporting Curiosity to You (C2U)

There is an element of joint attention that I'd like to give specific attention to here. The autistic individual's specific curiosity to the caregiver or the other person in an interaction is the key element that seems to be less accessed. I call this critical element of joint attention Curiosity to You or C2U.

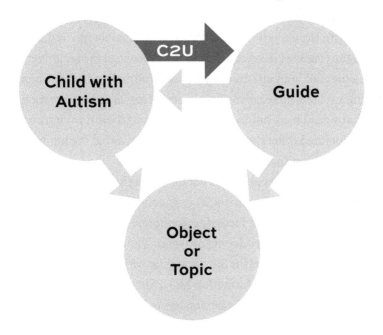

Visualize a triangle where two of the points represent the two people in a given interaction, and the third point represents an object or topic of mutual attention. Very young children with autism tend to gaze or talk about a topic or object but not readily gaze curiously toward the person with whom they are engaging. This lack of curious gazing to one's caregiver begins the breakdown of social reciprocity, resulting in the cascade effect. The autistic individual may focus primarily on the object or toy rather than looking to their caregiver for information, perspective, or shared emotion. In other words, their joint attention no longer includes the other person's experience of that object or topic—it no longer includes the social reciprocity.

It seems that the early back-and-forth social reciprocity weakens with the introduction of objects or topics. The curiosity to the caregiver gets either lost or significantly reduced in the course of development. This challenge to the reciprocity element of joint attention causes difficulties later in life when interactions increase in complexity. Much of the information that would have helped that child expand their thinking and understand others' emotions through nonverbal communication is then either lost or severely restricted.

Autistic adults give us a window into the processing difficulties associated with social engagements. They will often share that looking at faces, for example, can be distracting at best and anxiety producing at worst. They describe sensory input as coming in all at the same time without a proper filter. I imagine sensory information like a fire hose of input that is so overwhelming that the person has to find ways to shut down, shut out, or fight the onslaught of information. And when they are simply managing this sensory overload, they are certainly not looking for any more information to add to the flood. They are no longer curious about their partner.

Being curious implies that you are in a state of seeking additional information. We only do this when we are in a state of what is called "regulation." This regulation cannot happen if you are in a state of sensory flooding or overwhelm. When you are in this type of crisis, you are barely able to manage the amount of information in front of you. You are simply going to become very hyper-focused on getting safe from potential harm. Our brains are brilliantly constructed to shut down regions for reasoning and language when in the face of danger. Our bodies register the experience and subsequently slow our digestion and increase our heart rate and breathing. We become ready to fight or flee the situation.

In 2006, researcher Dr. Britta Renner summarized the importance of social curiosity by stating that "interest in how other people behave, think, and feel appears to be a fundamental prerequisite of human relationships." This study also evaluated the inverse relationship between anxiety and curiosity: the more anxious you are, the less likely you are to be curious, especially about other people. To put it another way, the more you are functioning from a physiological response to threat, the less action you take in social situations to gain additional information.

From Coregulation to Self-Regulation
Earlier I explained that children who later develop autism begin their lives like everyone else, with the drive to connect with their caregivers through what is called social reciprocity. When the additional layers of more people, objects, and awareness should be solidifying what is called joint attention, the autistic child attends more to the objects or topics to the exclusion of their caregivers. I postulate that this may be due to the experience described by adults on the spectrum of being overwhelmed by sensory information as social environments gain in complexity. With challenges to attention shifting, the child learns to find the predictability of objects and topics of interest safe and manageable. Predictability and sameness become comforts in contrast to the perceived chaos of sensory and social information.

In typical development, children use social reciprocity to gain understanding of the world around them. They may see something that they perceive as startling, but they look to their caregiver who looks calm and unfettered, so they borrow that calm from them to continue exploring. In autism, instead of social reciprocity and joint attention providing the child with reassurance, they are left to their own devices. Turning toward the more predictable elements in the environment becomes a mechanism to cope, to feel safe and grounded. Therefore the child may become rigid in routines or play—getting extremely agitated if something is out of place or is not as expected. That may be their safe zone, and if it's altered, their neurological system indicates danger, creating a state of crisis within the child's system.

In typical development, we are not born to self-soothe or socially engage right away. We are primed to look to others to help us with basic survival. At birth we are equipped to recognize our primary caregivers' voices. When we hear our caregivers, we might cry to indicate our discomfort so that they will offer nourishment, warmth, or security. Our caregiver responds to our vocalizations in a contingent manner, which begins the dance of social reciprocity. This early dance serves to help us regain biological homeostasis. We feel distress in our bodies, and when caregivers offer their regulated state and support, we return to calm.

In 1997, professor of psychology, Dr. Alan Fogel coined the term "coregulation" to define this mutual engagement between parent and child. It requires both infant and caregiver to be actively attending to and responding to one another in this contingent manner I have described. If one member in this dance is not regulated, the feedback loop halts or becomes out of sync. Through this dance or coregulation with our primary caregivers, we slowly but surely develop more internal mechanisms to manage the sensory input around us. We learn to regulate ourselves by first coregulating with caregivers, engaging in back-and-forth interactions that give rise to our internal self-regulation. When we are not regulated as children, a caregiver may pick us up, feed us, rock us, or otherwise attend to our needs until we regain regulation. And as we grow, we learn to internalize and trust our own ability to manage the world with confidence and competence based on those early experiences.

In 2017 a group in Italy published a study summarizing the essential nature of both members of that early engagement dance. The mother and the child in the communication dance of social reciprocity and coregulation are both essential for setting the stage for that child's future development. Tenuta, Marcone, Bartolo, Persampieri, and Costabile reported "the importance of the first mother–child communicative interaction: the circular dyadic interaction observed during the study proves to be an important factor for the growth of the child and for the consciousness of the maternal role" (Tenuta et al. 2017, 8). In other words, it is not just one member of this early pair that is essential but both members. The mutual exchanges within the first few months of life set a child up for more complex joint attention as they get older.

We can observe in young children at home, and then later in school-age students on the playground, that a child's developmental need for growth requires them to move beyond the confines of that parent-caregiver interaction and into more complex situations. Development "demands a widening of an infant's horizons beyond the mother's face to include other animate objects and their actions as well as inanimate objects and their motions" (Kaye and Fogel and Kay 1980). In fact, by the age of two years old, children are looking to socially engage in partnerships with other children using social reciprocity and joint attention.

When our caregivers lend us their regulated state, it becomes our own internal regulated state over time. When we perceive danger or uncertainty, we rely on the foundations defined here as social reciprocity and joint attention. Things in life get messy, complicated, and unpredictable. In fact, other people and our relationships with them are some of the most unpredictable, ever-changing aspects to our humanity. Without the underpinnings of social engagement, we are otherwise at the mercy of our sensory systems.

The Importance of Personal Agency

Next, let us move to the concept of what is called "personal agency." When we are born, we have very little personal agency, meaning we have very little control over what happens to us. We are at the whim of our physical needs and can only react to them with cries or other vocalizations. These actions are considered reactionary as they do not require thought and decision-making.

As we develop, we learn to engage in the environment with agency, reflection, decision-making, and foresight. We move from being reactive to being responsive in our interactions with others and the environment. The shift to responsiveness demonstrates the child's realization and understanding of our own unique or personal agency. We wake up to the understanding that our actions can make waves within the environment around us. We can make decisions based not on impulse but on our own unique experiences, memories, and goals.

Personal agency is essential to discovering who we are in the context of the world. We learn our preferences, our interests, and our personalities through interactions with the world that stretch and exercise our personal agency. While personal agency in adults is complex, mired in both thought and action, personal agency in an infant is found in the simple acts of movement with intention. A child learns that their actions are unique to themselves and can change the environment in front of them. If they push cereal off their high chair onto the floor, they hear it hit the floor, and maybe the dog comes joyfully running to assist. The child learns that their movements cause the mobile above their crib to bounce, leading to them taking deliberate action to make it happen again. The child learns that when they smile, their caregiver smiles, and when they vocalize, their caregiver vocalizes in response. The child learns that they have personal agency.

When a person does not have or develop adequate personal agency, they become dependent on the decisions of others for their well-being. They will do one of two things: become completely compliant and withdrawn, unable to make decisions for themselves, or fight prompts, becoming defiant while still being unable to make decisions for themselves. The goal seems to be somewhere in between, or maybe both. We strive for interdependence, where we can make decisions for ourselves based on a multitude of mini-experiments where we put ourselves out there and make discoveries while also respecting, considering, and collaborating with others who have different life experiences than our own. It is through social reciprocity and joint attention that we learn to borrow the intentions and decision-making of others, which then become our own for this incredibly rewarding and complex experience of social engagement.

When Behaviors and Interests Become Restricted or Repetitive

You may be wondering how the second criteria for the diagnosis of autism—restricted or repetitive behaviors—fits into this equation or cascade effect. Good question! For someone to be diagnosed with autism, they must also exhibit restricted or repetitive interests or behaviors, which may look like a narrowed focus on certain topics or activities to the detriment of others. I'll share with you how this symptom is a result of the change in developmental trajectory described in this chapter. But first, let me describe the symptom a bit more specifically.

Simply put, this diagnostic symptom refers to a person's outward behaviors that seem rigid, limited, or repetitive. It refers to the behaviors you commonly see in the movies or read about in the news. It is not dependent on the person's cognitive ability or level of independence. This is where you see a wide range of behaviors and the spectrum of autism. A person may demonstrate the classic hand flapping or rocking for self-soothing. Or a person may need to walk a certain route every time they go to the grocery store, getting upset or disoriented if they are required to veer from that usual route. Another manifestation may be for a person to pursue reading in-depth about history or even theology, but not be able to put it into use in a professional setting. An interest like this has limits to its application.

As I mentioned earlier in this book, my first introduction to autism was through an eight-year-old boy at a weekend respite camp. While he was mostly nonspeaking, he would jump up and down, hitting his middle fingers on the ground, while waiting in line for the cafeteria with me. He did not seem stressed. The behavior seemed more like the way some of us may twirl our hair or bite our nails. He seemed to enjoy the way it felt to jump and land, feeling his body in space and tapping the ground with his fingers, as if to be sure it was still there. This boy was demonstrating the repetitive behaviors of autism.

Another way to understand the restrictedness of autistic behaviors is to consider what we call "splinter skills." Some people with autism have special abilities that seem far above the other areas of their development. It is common for a person's motor development or memory for facts to be at or above age level while their language development lags behind. Some may be considered autistic savants—being able to sing, play the piano, or solve Rubik's Cubes in seconds and with such exactness that it rivals their other areas of development. Still others may have particular special interests in which they excel. They may draw with extreme preciseness and detail, recall a plethora of facts about trains, or use a computer to access preferred videos even when they still do not get themselves dressed independently.

And still others demonstrate the restricted or repetitive interests or behaviors by hyper-focusing on one topic or activity while neglecting or ignoring others.

A two-year-old in my practice, for example, routinely fixated on stacking alphabet blocks. She would stack them so that the letters on the blocks lined up just so, getting agitated when they fell or when someone tried to intervene playfully. She was seemingly not open to expanding that play into building other things or playing with them in an imaginary manner. A teen in my practice would ask incessant questions of his parents and support workers about the social rules by which he was required to abide. For example, he wanted to engage with his peers but was confused by the fact that when at work, he was not allowed to talk. While many gave him what seemed like logical explanations, he remained "stuck" and repeated the same questions to those around him. And several adults in my practice enjoy playing complex strategy games such as Dungeons & Dragons, chess, or Settlers of Catan—able to remember facts, figures, and rules better than most at their age, but struggling to strategize their own independence with peers and employment.

Summarizing the Developmental Cascade Effect

As children, we engage with our caregivers in quiet, relaxed environments before we are tasked with navigating more dynamic situations. Children who develop autism may become overwhelmed and need to retreat inward for neurobiological safety. The new, more complex environments (additional people, lights, sounds, smells, and touch) may feel harsh and be too much for their neurological and biological systems. Instead they feel flooded by sensory information, so they shut down additional stimuli in favor of sameness, routine, and predictability. To compensate, the child may learn to focus on things in the environment that are predictable and within their control. To calm their systems, they find rhythmic motions, line things up, or rely on other repetitive behaviors for soothing. Here is where you see the restrictive and repetitive behaviors and interests. People on the autism spectrum use these as defense mechanisms to keep themselves feeling safe. Routines, rituals, and sameness become focal points from which to understand and interact with the world.

It is through our ability to engage with our world in a dynamic, ever-changing manner that helps define us, define who we want to be in the future, and define how we impact those around us. The insistence on sameness for a person's sense of security leads to disappointment when other people offer their ideas and contributions in play or employment. Humans, even others with autism, all have unique and unpredictable ways of interacting. Successful social development relies on our ability to be curious and integrate how others may see the world around us.

At autism's core lies the divergence in social reciprocity resulting in restricted or repetitive interests or behaviors. Sensory sensitivities, plus challenges with shifting attention, cause a disruption in the natural development and timing of back-and-forth engagement with caregivers. While this early social reciprocity is proven to be intact, it is the added complexity that causes the person to no longer be able to access or use that framework for later development. Being able to jointly attend to something with loved ones becomes less manageable, enjoyable, and useful. This disruption leads to the cascade effect affecting regulation, understanding one's own personal agency, and one's impact on the world. Routines and sameness become refuges for security and intellectual growth.

Everything you see in autism (e.g., sensory sensitivities, social withdrawal, repetition of sounds or phrases) all happens in typical development—but in autism, it is a matter of extremes. People with autism can experience sensory sensitivities that render them unable to leave the house without noise-cancelling headphones to dampen the input. Others may have such severe sensitivity to touch that water in a shower feels like painfully sharp pins and needles. Some autistic people also experience synesthesia, a crossover between senses (such as seeing colors with sounds). Some experience emotions and people's energy as colors or hues. While some of us may experience sensory sensitivities, they are not usually to the extreme that they limit our ability to interact with the world.

CHAPTER 2

Sensory and Emotional Flooding

Flooding: (n) 1. A sensation of feeling psychologically and physically overwhelmed during conflict, making it virtually impossible to have a productive problem-solving discussion.
—The Gottman Institute

For years people assumed that autistic people did not feel emotions in themselves or recognize them in others. By consulting with autistic adults, we now know this may be the exact opposite of the truth. They actually feel emotions more intensely than many of us. It is the ability to organize and make sense of those emotions in themselves and others that is confusing and overwhelming, causing them to either shut down or have what seem like overreactions.

A young child, for example, may quickly get overwhelmed by sensory input and emotions. The parent's well-intentioned sound effects and words combine with the child's own stress level and may add to the overwhelm rather than alleviate it. A kind and otherwise generous child may not be able to attend to a peer who is upset due to the onslaught of sensory and social information happening around them. Instead this child may use behaviors that challenge themselves or others to regain clarity and temporary control. A teen or adult may retreat to their room rather than being able to figure out how to manage their own internal emotional rollercoaster. Add your frustration or disappointment to the mix, and the teen or adult goes into full shutdown mode.

A man I have coached for approximately one year is exploring how we "feel" other people's emotions. He is a very logical and concrete thinker, so he is not prone to simply believing that something happens due to its magical or spiritual qualities. He wants to figure out why and how he is overwhelmed by other people's emotional states. He describes his experience as taking in enormous amounts of detailed information around him constantly. The information includes people's facial expressions, gestures, and postures, in addition to the visual and auditory clutter that surrounds us at all times. The lights, sounds, colors, and movements around us result in a cacophony of sensory information.

He uses an analogy to explain his experience: a computer would overheat under these circumstances and stop working. He posits that he is simply taking in too much sensory information for his own system to manage, prioritize, and organize efficiently.

So in keeping with this understanding that people with autism are commonly and especially sensitive to the detailed information around them while being unable to successfully prioritize and manage it, we must pay particular attention to the elements we add as their partners. Your stress, your tension, and your low expectations of the autistic individual probably only add to that flood of sensory and emotional information. If you wish to engage, partner, and guide someone on the autism spectrum, your ability to be and stay regulated when engaging is critical. If you are anxious or overwhelmed, your partner in the interaction may react to that anxiety before you even have a chance to open your mouth to mitigate. Your emotions can be felt as "noise" that comes in as chaotic and difficult to manage.

I'd like for you to imagine starting your day with a full cup of coffee, water, or tea. Each day we hopefully have been refreshed with sleep, which represents our restart, our full cup. As we go through the day, situations arise that require us to drink from that cup. These situations are neither positive nor negative; they are simply situations that our minds and bodies manage. We get dressed; we take a sip. We gather up our essentials for the day, and we take another sip. But then we are a little late for work, the news on the radio is upsetting, or the radio announcer's voice is slightly annoying. Oof. Take a big sip. We are already looking at the bottom of our cup. It is almost empty. We sit down in our comfy chair ready to work. We turn on our computer, and it crashes, showing us only a pixelated screen (yes, this might have happened in the middle of writing this book). We sit back in our chair and drink the rest of the contents of our cup trying to think of what to do next. But then we are spent. We are depleted. Feelings of anxiety creep in as we realize our deadlines won't be met and our online appointments will all need to be shifted. We are so overwhelmed with the new and added responsibilities that we stare at the computer screen, frozen.

That depleted and overwhelmed feeling is familiar to a lot of us, but for people with autism, it reportedly happens regularly, maybe all of the time. Both autistics and neurotypicals need to figure out what works for us to rejuvenate or refill our cups throughout the day or week to be at our best. When we are depleted, our decision-making capacity and ability to take action are severely limited.

"Neurotypical" describes development that progresses in a routine and similar manner for the majority of people. Autism is an example of "neurodiversity," when development is different than the typical progression.

Spoon Theory and Token Theory

The spoon theory was first described by Christine Miserandino, who has a diagnosis of lupus. She used this analogy to explain to her friends about the decisions she had to make regarding her energy levels. She shared that she starts the day with a certain number of spoons and has to make choices throughout the day as to where she spends those spoons. Something as simple as having a shower or making herself breakfast may take a certain number of spoons, while something more fun may take an equal amount, even though it is enjoyable. The point is that once she is out of spoons, she is no longer able to engage and must shut down to rejuvenate. She may start her day with ten spoons, for example. Activities of daily living are included in those things that take spoons. Doing the dishes might take two or three of her limited number of spoons. She may have to choose which activity is most important that day to have enough energy left over for work or socializing with friends. Otherwise, she will run out of spoons or energy and not be able to function.

The autistic community has adopted this analogy but with an arcade theme: you start each day with a certain number of tokens to play the game of life. You choose which games or activities to play throughout a given day, but when you have depleted your token stash, you simply cannot play anymore—until you rejuvenate and gain more tokens.

Rejuvenating will look different for each person. Here are some common ways people with autism spectrum disorders rejuvenate—and if you're neurotypical, you might find them helpful as well:

- Gazing off into space for a bit of time between interactions
- Getting into something that is very intellectual or concrete, like building or organizing items
- Finding a cozy, dark place to sit for a while
- Venting to someone who simply listens without trying to solve
- Laying down and sleeping for a few minutes
- Engaging in very routine and predictable activities, like walking a typical route or watching a movie they have seen many times
- Repeating words or questions over and over, even if they have heard or seem to know the answer

- Taking a day in between busy days to be by themselves and have uninterrupted quiet
- Making lists or following routines that reduce the decision-making load

Even if a child or adult is not reliably verbal, they can and still do experience the same wide range of emotions as the rest of us. And they may feel your emotions more than you realize, with a lot less ability to make sense of them. Your stress adds to the flood of stress, emotion, or sensory onslaught they are experiencing. If you are hurt, scared, worried, nervous, happy, surprised, or excited, the person with whom you are engaging may feel that intensity whether you intend it or not. Even the fact that we have more than one emotion at once can be overwhelming and confusing—for example, feeling happy and anxious at the same time.

So even without intending it, your emotions, your stress, and your energy, in addition to your words and actions, can be adding to the flood that the person with autism is trying to manage with limited energy tokens or spoons. But you have the power to reduce that noise for your child, partner, or friend. Taking care of yourself can be key to reducing the noise of your emotional reactions. We will go into this a bit more deeply in the next chapter, "Your Own Self-Care and Well-Being." By using self-soothing strategies, you can reduce the input for the autistic person with whom you wish to engage. Help them hear and connect with you by taking good care of yourself so that you can show up with your cool, calm, and collected self. Taking care of yourself is the *most* important thing you can do with and for a person with autism.

Prepare for Challenging Times

I may be stating the obvious, but loving someone with autism (or anyone, honestly) can be challenging at times. You need to replenish your own spoons as much as they need to replenish theirs. Taking care of yourself will help you weather the storms of behaviors, arguments, disagreements, and misunderstandings. As you will read in chapter 3, learning to regulate yourself refers to your ability to manage the complexity of your environment without going into what is known as flight, fight, freeze, or faint. This is also known as reacting from your limbic system. Staying calm in your own body, or at least knowing how to regain a neutral state, will help you stay clear-headed, kind, and compassionate.

Taking the time to focus on yourself is truly the most ideal thing you can do to build and maintain your relationships with those with autism in your life. While people with autism are amazing in so many ways, you may also encounter moments that are not typical to many relationships. You will need to be ready to weather the storms when they come.

While most of the time, autistics are the most honest, loyal, kind, and compassionate people, at other times their reactions can be perplexing, quite unsettling, or even scary.

- You may have a younger child who gets aggressive out of frustration at the slightest change in schedule. They may scream, cry, and even hit their head on the floor.
- You may have an older child or teen who destroys property in your home, threatens you or others with violence, engages in self-injury, or even talks about suicide.
- You may have an adult friend, spouse, partner, or client who tries with all their might to stay regulated, but when

the stress builds up, they blow up instead. They might not yet be diagnosed and so may not realize their own personal challenges with regulation. They may get in your face, screaming, crying, or threatening you.

In the challenging moments when you are getting increasingly frustrated and starting to lose your temper (we all do, sometimes), it will take great inner strength for you to stay calm and collected. Usually if you are escalating in the face of your child or partner's escalation, you are making some assumptions about the reasons behind their behavior. Remember: when faced with sensory or information overload, the autistic person may be reacting from a different and necessary neurological state. They may be reacting as if you and the environment are a danger; therefore, they may push you away, leave, or become aggressive to themselves or others. It is due to their neurological system being on overload rather than being due to their trying to "get your goat," "get attention," or "push your buttons."

In most cases, it has nothing to do with you specifically—unless you make things worse by escalating too. You may have to ensure safety and silently give them space so they can return to a calmer state, or they may need your solid, steady, regulated, and reassuring silence. Both of these responses from you will require your being as healthy and centered as possible while ensuring an amazing foundation for your child or partner from which to regain regulation.

To bring this point home, if you react as if the person is trying to control you, you are also assuming an incredible capacity for them to control their own regulatory system. You are assuming they can control their own neurological response while also considering your mental state, needs, and thoughts. Please make note that if, on a good day, they struggle to understand their impact on others, how on earth could they be able to do that in a conniving way just to manipulate you while they are overwhelmed?

A teenage client who was quite capable in many areas of his life struggled significantly with regulation. While he was adept in creating videos on social media, had a girlfriend he loved and adored, and had an incredible sense of social justice, he struggled. Whenever he experienced a series of changes to his schedule that built up over a short period of time (e.g., a new school, substitute teachers, kitchen remodel, sibling distress, or even frustration with being interrupted from his focus on a game), he would first say, "Stop it" or "You don't get it!" He would then escalate to the next level, where he would start swearing, trying to leave, or toppling tables. Kind and well-meaning adults surrounding him would try to reason with him, talk to him, or lecture him when he was starting to escalate—only making it more overwhelming and adding to the flood. His behaviors were frightening and limiting his access to the community.

But with loving and supportive caregivers who learned to stay calm, steady, and silent, he learned to borrow their regulation in those moments to regain his composure. If he could not reregulate for whatever reason, he learned to leave the situation rather than escalate. This took extensive practice—not only for him to desensitize, but also for him to learn his own ability to stay regulated in the face of changes and unexpected additions to his environment.

By understanding the sensory and emotional flood experienced by those with autism, we can show up in a way that will help you both maintain or regain composure and dignity. By showing up calmly when they are no longer regulated (commonly referred to as "dysregulated" by therapists), you bring your thinking to the situation. You can reflect on the situational factors that may have accumulated to cause the overload. Then when everyone is regulated again, you can "return to the flag," as one of my clients aptly named the moment that things went off course. By addressing the situation later, when all are calm and regulated, you can come to new understandings and new ways of managing those same situations that were triggers.

Dysregulated, Not Incapable

Autistic teens or adults may not need guidance in all realms of their lives. Just because they struggle with regulation doesn't mean they are not incredibly capable in other ways. You may look to them for their expertise or natural ability in academics or intellectual facts, for example. A parent may rely on the studious child to do well in school academically. You may look to the autistic adult to guide you in politics or finances. I know that I have been blessed with my autistic partner's knowledge about biology, medical details, politics, and investing. And that same person may look to you and your expertise in being social and staying regulated when they become overwhelmed or flooded with sensory information.

If a person is dysregulated a lot of the time, they may appear to be less capable overall. Sometimes it is very hard to determine a person's capabilities if they are constantly in hypervigilant mode, which means they're always neurologically perceiving a threat. Once you figure out how to best support someone with regulation needs, you may uncover their true abilities.

It can be confusing when someone who does so extraordinarily well in some areas struggles so much with their own sensory and emotional regulation. But that is the crux of autism. So keep your composure. Do not take things personally. It can be quite difficult to remember to not take things personally when interacting with an infant, child, teen, or adult, with autism.

You may have an infant who does not play peekaboo with you, or they become agitated with your attempts to soothe, or they seem to want to be left alone a lot of the time. These kinds of reactions or seeming preferences of your sweet baby can be devastating to a parent. You may feel that your child is rejecting you. You must keep in mind that a baby's system has to also be ready and available for the back-and-forth feedback loop and social engagement. If they are simply trying to stay regulated in their own bodies, they may be experiencing states of sensory overwhelm, chaos, and flooding. They may be in a state of hypervigilance and/or avoidance that may feel essential for their self-preservation. Their responses are neurological, not personal.

A child may seek control by creating predictable scenarios with you. This may look like asking you the same question over and over, or it may look like aggressive behavior that has a predictable response. The child uses these to create a sense of safety in the midst of what they may perceive as chaos. It is neurological, not personal.

An adult may get awash with irritation, embarrassment, or sadness. Instead of apologizing or taking ownership, they may lash out with words that hurt. It is neurological, not personal.

As humans, when our neurological systems are overwhelmed, it can kick in the very instinctual and physical response of shutting down the thinking parts of our brains. When this happens, we may go into fight, flight, freeze, or faint. Thankfully our brains are wired to support us when we are in danger. Instead of entering deep thought and contemplation when faced with a snarling dog or bear, we shut down the thinking and speaking parts of our brains to either fight, run, hide, or play dead. Quite literally, when we are in this heightened state, the parts of our brains in charge of reasoning and language go offline so as to conserve all energy for running away or fighting the danger perceived. It is not a time for listening, reflecting, or finding common ground on disagreements. This heightened state would never be a time to lecture, teach, or guide. When interacting with an autistic person in this state, it is only a time to stop, reduce stimuli, and allow the neurological and biological systems in both of you to calm and return to baseline.

We each spend much of our time in what is our regulated state, the window where we stay regulated. But sometimes things start to bother us, stress us, or aggravate us. If it is just one thing, we may be able to be flexible and manage it pretty well. However, if we have two, three, or an increasing number of those things in a short amount of time without time to recover in between, we may climb the wave of escalation and even get to a point when we explode, say things we wish we hadn't, get aggressive with our words or actions, or completely shut down without being able to engage with the world as we can when we are regulated.

As you can see in the diagram, the top of the wave represents a sensory or emotional storm. In the middle of that storm, the only thing to do is to batten down the hatches and keep yourself and everyone safe. It is not a time for teaching, engaging, lecturing, or guiding. Save your breath. Allow yourself and the person who is in the middle of the storm to simply allow the storm to pass—while keeping everyone safe, of course. Take note of what seemed to lead up to it when you reflect on the escalation later. You can process the events, sensory inputs, and scenarios when you are regulated again—when you can make logical and sound decisions for how to handle things differently next time.

Aim for the Window

In trauma-informed care and teaching, there is something called the "window of tolerance." Inside the window of tolerance is the zone in which we can function, live, and thrive without extreme fear and without slipping into the limbic regions of our brains, which are outside of that window. The limbic regions are designed for hypervigilance and to keep us safe from imminent danger.

I was recently introduced to a children's book titled *Hey Warrior* by Karen Young that refers to this region as a "warrior," which I find helpful in explaining anxiety in the body. This limbic region tries very hard to protect us but sometimes goes into overdrive—doing more than we and our bodies actually need in a given moment or situation—which then looks and feels like anxiety.

Dr. Daniel Siegel describes the window of tolerance as a river with two banks. One bank represents the experience of chaos, while the other bank represents rigidity and shutdown. Our goal is to flow easily down the river without hitting either bank. In autism, the river seems very narrow. The person very easily and quickly slips out of the optimal window into fight, flight, freeze, or faint. They may hit the riverbanks and get hung up in either chaos or rigidity rather than finding a flow. A way of using these analogies in relation to autism may be to think about the window being only open a very small amount or the river being extremely narrow. The edges are close, and the likelihood that the person will be reacting from the bank of rigidity or chaos is great.

In classrooms and intervention settings across the globe, you may see colors used to signify levels of stress that individuals are experiencing. These are very similar to those you see in emergency medical facilities to rate one's level of pain. The red zone represents the fight-or-flight feeling, the blue represents freeze or faint, and the green zone represents the optimal window of tolerance. Many classrooms use something called "The 5-Point Scale," or renditions of it, to guide children in understanding their own escalations while discovering solutions for recovery. The additional colors in the 5-Point Scale represent more levels of a person's regulation, with green being "calm" and red being "I'm going to explode." I find it excruciating that we commonly ask individuals with autism to rate their own regulation and expect them to make choices about how to calm themselves when we do very little to help them understand their own processing in the first place. Therefore, I have adapted these tools to help those around that person. Parents, teachers, partners, and caregivers can understand the signs and signals that the person may provide unconsciously that can indicate times for us to step in (or out) to optimally support their regulation. These unconscious signs can include movements, facial expressions, and sounds indicating escalating distress.

Through supportive relationships and the partnering we will discuss in chapter 11, "Creating Partnerships," we can be guides for individuals with autism to successfully find the flow of the river. By widening their window or river, we can carry them to new destinations for more successful and independent living.

I had a client years ago who was very kind and engaging in our group sessions; in contrast, he would seemingly out of nowhere jump up and grab some item to be used as a weapon that he wielded at to others in the group. By observing him closely, I was able to determine both what his body did and at what particular moments he would start to escalate. When he was asked a question that he was not sure of the answer, his eyes would start to dart around the room, for example. He would then start moving his body in a rocking-type motion and sometimes start pacing. This combination of movements indicated to me that he was moving into the limbic regions of his brain—something was activating his fight response. By seeing the escalation before the storm was at full capacity, I was able to ensure his and everyone's safety in the group.

Self-Regulation as an Attainable Goal

Research into the development of regulation in humans leads us to wonder whether it is reasonable to ask children where their stress levels are and leave them to figure out ways to alleviate their own stress. The prefrontal cortex is not yet fully developed and will not be for quite some time—not until they're about twenty-five years old. Most adults would struggle with assessing their own personal stress levels in order to then select options for their own calming.

That's why, in my practice, I have shifted the conversation from the child determining their own stress levels to asking the parents or adults to explore the escalation stages for themselves first and then their child. The first step is to observe one's resting state. Then note each stage as you escalate with stress or input. Observe what works and what doesn't in your life for keeping yourself and your autistic child, partner, or friend in a regulated state. Notice what alleviates stress and what aggravates it further. Being able to understand what is stressful for individuals in addition to what sends them onto the riverbanks of chaos or rigidity can be a helpful step to alleviate or avoid situations.

While being calm all the time seems like a good idea, we all need to challenge ourselves slightly beyond our current ability and comfort zones to learn and grow optimally. Child psychologist Lev Vygotsky called this the "zone of proximal development." It is similar to the window of tolerance, the river of well-being, and the green zone in that it is the sensory and emotional environment where the person finds learning manageable and ideal. In stretching the zone or the window, we will cause escalations. If we don't, we may not be challenging the person to new levels of learning. In the next chapter, we will explore your own self-care and well-being so that you can observe at the level necessary for determining someone's zone of proximal development while being ready to weather the storms of learning.

CHAPTER 3

Your Own Self-Care and Well-Being

Showing kindness toward those who are different, and embracing our imperfections as proof of our humanness, is the remedy for fear.
—Emma Zurcher-Long

There are three ways to consider taking care of yourself. All three are essential in order for you to be the grounding and compassionate individual you wish to be with the child or person with autism in your life. If you have autism yourself, these are certainly also applicable to you.

1. Overall healthcare and wellness
2. Couple or relationship care with other adults in your life
3. In-the-moment self-soothing

First, take a few moments to consider your overall health and well-being. Think about the things that keep you at your best.

Some people rely on their morning coffee—that would be me—and without it would feel quite out of sorts. Some also rely on exercise or time with friends to keep their mental clarity and energy. And still others may rely on alone time to rejuvenate their well-being. There are lots of ways to think about what keeps you at your best.

Neuroscience thought leaders Dr. David Rock and Dr. Daniel Siegel co-created the "Healthy Mind Platter" for evaluating where we may be out of balance and how to consider adjustments. They include seven essential mind activities to keep yourself optimally healthy. The idea is that each of us ensure time spent in each of the areas of the platter for full and satisfied living. Dr. Rock and Dr. Siegel describe the seven areas that should ideally be in balance with one another as follows:

- Focus Time: When we closely focus on tasks in a goal-oriented way, taking on challenges that make deep connections in the brain.
- Play Time: When we allow ourselves to be spontaneous or creative, playfully enjoying novel experiences, which helps make new connections in the brain.
- Connecting Time: When we connect with other people, ideally in person, or take time to appreciate our connection to the natural world around us, richly activating the brain's relational circuitry.
- Physical Time: When we move our bodies, aerobically if medically possible, which strengthens the brain in many ways.
- Time In: When we quietly reflect internally, focusing on sensations, images, feelings and thoughts, helping to better integrate the brain.

- Down Time: When we are non-focused, without any specific goal, and let our mind wander or simply relax, which helps the brain recharge.
- Sleep Time: When we give the brain the rest it needs to consolidate learning and recover from the experiences of the day.

Many life and business coaches use life balance wheels to guide their clients. They have the same premise: in order to feel balanced, we must ensure health in each of the areas of our lives. The wheel can be used as an assessment to guide our process for considering areas in our lives that are out of balance. The wheel also can guide us to create goals for ourselves in unbalanced areas for better, more well-rounded living. There are official life balance wheels you can choose from by doing a simple internet search. Most are arranged in a circle with each spoke of the wheel representing an area of life. Here are common areas seen on life balance wheels:

- Spirituality
- Health
- Social
- Recreation
- Family
- Service/Community
- Finance
- Career/Study
- Relationships/Love

One of my wonderful clients was sharing recently about her latest celebrations and frustrations surrounding her son's toilet training, school experiences, and some challenging behaviors. In the midst of her update, she paused and shared that she had stayed up way too late reading a book "just for fun." She had been so concerned that staying up late would then make things so hard the next day with parenting. She was thrilled to learn that she was not as tired as she thought she would be but was fed by reading a fun book just for herself.

I am certainly not advocating for staying up and missing sleep, but if you are doing it for fun reasons once in a while, it may not be such a bad idea! Remember to spend time with friends, books, hobbies, and the outdoors—even if you have to stretch a little to do them. They may feed your energy in ways you may not have predicted.

With my clients and in my trainings, I sometimes suggest they use what I call the Sun Diagram to help them determine things that feel good and essential for their overall well-being. Try it out! In the center of the sun, I ask you to put your picture, a drawing, or simply your name. Then place something on each ray of the sun that represents something keeps you at your best.

Regardless of which way you choose to assess your own needs around self-care and well-being, take some time to select one or two things that you need for your overall health so you can truly show up for your child, partner, family members, friends, and acquaintances. Determine which ones may need a bit more of your attention. Remember: people around you respond to your regulation as soon as you walk in the room—especially those on the spectrum. It is like a ripple effect. You can either walk in the room rumbling and subsequently creating additional chaos, or you can bring calm that spreads amongst others. Calming your own system can do wonders so that you can be welcoming to those around you.

Self-care is an essential part of your repertoire of intervention for your child, student, or partner. It is an active ingredient for connecting more deeply with your partner with autism. By attending to your own regulation, you are more likely to be more open, aware, and thoughtful—all of which will enhance your interactions. Do not think of self-care as extra credit to be done only if you have spare time. Self-care must be central to building successful relationships and bonds with others. Instead of feeling guilty for taking that time for yourself, consider it the best thing you can do to be there for others—not just in physical presence, but in mental capacity as well.

Is Your Stress Contagious?

Some people with autism can clearly demonstrate through their behaviors when they are feeling your stress. With others it may be more subtle. Some people can tell you verbally that they are stressed, but most will show you they are overwhelmed by getting more routinized or having more challenging behaviors. They may become agitated, cranky, and out of sorts, or they may become aggressive, angry, and mean. As a more subtle sign, they may retreat, becoming either lethargic or extremely hyper-focused on routines and predictableness, then falling apart when and if something does not go as planned for them. I hate to tell you, but even when you think you are hiding your stress, you probably aren't.

A couple with twins, both with autism, started service with me due to struggles with their boys fighting regularly and getting aggressive with peers at school. We spent the first two months of our work together helping both parents find their own calm. We used the Sun Diagram to determine activities they needed to ensure they were able to bring their own best selves to their sons.

Then we moved to ensuring their relationship as a couple so that communication between them could be at its best (not going for perfect, mind you—just ensuring communication was happening and could be productive). We explored the couple's and their sons' regulation stages, as discussed in the previous chapter. We worked on ways for them to care for themselves when they were escalated by their sons' behaviors. They learned how to prioritize self- and couple care so that they could be more responsive rather than reactive. They learned how to slow down and observe first before intervening too soon.

I remember them saying that just their ability to take the time to observe before stepping in to intervene was incredibly helpful for them to bring their best thinking to their parenting in tough moments. They learned to give ample processing time and use wording that allowed the boys to think and process their own reactions with one another.

They reported that the changes in their sons' behaviors and engagements were significant and faster than expected. The parents moved deliberately from a place of reacting to their sons' fights with anger to now being able to observe calmly and step in when or if it was really necessary. They learned to be curious before reacting. Their sons' aggressive behaviors reduced significantly, and the family became much better able to enjoy their time together.

Caring for Your Other Relationships

I do not need to tell you that it can be quite consuming to worry that you or your client, young child, teen, or companion may have autism and then field the countless opinions thrown at you. There are so many options and opinions swirling around you all of the time that can make you question your decisions. People will give you advice and tell you not to worry, as well as trying to make you fearful that time is being wasted. If you are concerned about your young child having autism, the pediatrician may tell you to "wait and see" when you know in your gut that you are not connecting with your infant or child as you feel you should. Scheduling appointments and waiting for each new glimmer of hope can be excruciating.

Receiving a diagnosis of autism at any age then lands you in a minefield full of decision-making with numerous recommendations and an equal number of strong opinions. Some well-meaning—but incorrect—professionals will tell you there is a window of opportunity that you do not want to miss in your child's development, or it will be too late. This is not true. Our brains are extremely adept at new learning and adaptability. We are constantly learning and making new connections based on our experiences, whether we have autism or not. You can start down one path of support and turn around. You can switch course later if it doesn't feel right. It is okay to change your mind or use several different approaches that you think might help you or someone you know with autism feel supported.

Many receiving a diagnosis want to find out everything there is to know about autism and how to cure it as soon as possible. They go into hyperdrive researching, learning, and fixing. They want the magic fix, as if autism is a disease to cure instead of a dense complexity of developmental, regulation, and sensory differences combined with a person's own experiences and personality. Getting to know the person as an individual, rather than choosing one specific intervention as a cure, is the key to connection and progress. When the dust settles from the assessments, your child or partner will still be there, ready to be seen by you.

Becoming your child's most amazing advocate cannot mean that you leave yourself behind. You need to be a serious superstar at self-care first, as I've already said, and that includes you having relationships with others outside of the autism-intervention world. Having relationships with others in your life is essential for keeping some perspective while having a community to support you and the person with autism. It may be cliché, but it's so often true that it takes a community or a village to raise our children and thrive together.

Relationships with friends, family members, partners, and others can be challenging and heart-wrenching. It is our personal responsibility to nurture ourselves and our other relationships with friends and family. We cannot be at our best if we get too narrowly focused on any one relationship, including that with your child or work.

Counselors, social workers, and psychologists confirm that we cannot get everything we need from any one relationship. It is in fact not healthy to do so, for us or for the other person. Each person in our lives can complement us while also challenging us. No one person can or should be expected to fulfill our happiness, our wholeness, or our balance.

If you're reading this book, you are probably spending a lot of time thinking about autism and the person or people in your life on the spectrum. The answer to your current hyper-focus on autism? Diversify. You have a lot of love to give. Do not worry that you need to give all of that love solely to the person with autism in your life. You have enough to go around. Having other relationships in your life will only make you feel more supported, loved, and seen as well. People want to show up for you and support you. Let them. People want to know the multiple facets of who you are—not just the parts of you that are autism related. Cultivate those relationships and conversations so that you feel like a whole person when you show up for yourself, your child, friend, loved one, or student. Maintain friendships with others who share your hobbies or interests. And if you don't have any hobbies or interests, try a few out. The biggest challenge is to not feel guilty when you let go and explore other relationships.

In my own first year of teaching, I was completely consumed by my work. I would arrive to school by 7:00 a.m. and not leave until 7:00 p.m. most days. I worked on weekends designing lesson plans and materials. I researched new ways of teaching, sharing, and delivering content. Even though I thought I was happy and thriving by giving my all, my friends and family were missing out. I would justify that my work was so important for the children in my care and their families that it was okay for me to neglect myself and my own loved ones. Well, I was careening quickly toward Burnout Cliff, and everyone could see it but me.

I'm not sure why I listened, but a speech pathologist serving my classroom pulled me aside one day. She shared her concerns and invited me to join a dragon boat team here in Portland, Oregon. They met at the crack of dawn out on the Willamette River to practice two to three times per week. They needed a flag catcher. I took the bait and committed to the team. This group of women turned out to be amazing and all breast-cancer survivors, as I am. They knew the importance of self-care and of having a community surrounding you to keep you strong.

My dragon-boating season with them taught me so much about keeping balance. I know I was stronger and more resilient in the classroom thanks to having something completely different in my life to complement my teaching.

You may find it helpful to take some time to consider who you were prior to having children or starting your career in working with people with disabilities. Your choice to take care of yourself in little ways can make a huge impact on your ability to help someone navigate our crazy, busy world. You will find some ideas for self-care in the back of this book. Please reference and use them often!

Couple and Relationship Care

If you are in a marriage or partnership with someone, cultivate that. It is very common for one parent to work extra hours to make enough money to fund different therapies, for example, and the other to stay home to raise children. This can create a "working relationship" but not necessarily an emotionally rewarding one. Whether you are both working in or out of the home, you will both have your ups and downs in the day, meeting only at the end of the day to vent, fall apart, or raise each other up. Here are some ideas taken from my practice that other couples have found helpful (and there are more in the first appendix):

SCHEDULE A ROUTINE DATE EACH WEEK

You don't even have to leave the house if you don't want to or can't for childcare reasons. Set up a spot in your house or yard to sit, or go to coffee or lunch together each week. Get to know each other again. Talk about interests, hobbies, jobs, or travel. Stretch yourselves to talk about other things rather than autism or childrearing.

MAKE AN END-OF-THE-DAY CHECK-IN A ROUTINE

The Gottman Institute recommends an end-of-the-day conversation that can be quite helpful. This is where each of you gets to vent to one another without trying to solve anything for the other person. It may sound like this: "Joey spilled a whole jar of honey all over the toaster today. I lost it and screamed at him." The other person has a choice of either trying to fix the issue by saying something like, "Wow. You shouldn't have screamed. What were you thinking?" or "I'll take care of it. I'll go talk to him." Using the Gottman approach instead, consider just listening and validating by saying something like, "That sounds really frustrating. You must have been really angry." Most of the time, we just want someone to be on our team and support us through the tough stuff, not to solve our problems. We can usually solve the problems ourselves, and if we cannot, we will ask for our partner's advice.

CREATE AN "END OF YOUR ROPE" CODE WORD

Create a code word for when you are at the end of your rope or have yourself completely escalated and need your partner to step in. This will ensure that you remain a united front in front of your child(ren) rather than undermining each other with comments like, "I just can't take this anymore," or "Why don't you do anything around here?" You can state your code word instead. "Peanut butter" may be the word you use to indicate to your coparent that you need them.

AVOID COACHING EACH OTHER IN THE MOMENT

Do not coach each other in the moment of parenting. This rarely works. Allow the other person to explore their own approach in a given moment and then talk about it afterward.

COMMIT AND BACK EACH OTHER UP ON HOUSEHOLD RULES OR EXPECTATIONS

Choose a time each week to discuss your household rules. Make revisions to the rules as needed. The bottom line is that you want to be a united front and support one another in the moment. Together, get clear on those household rules, so choose one to three to target at a time. These can be such things as eating only at the table or using kind words in the house with each other. Together, decide which are the most important ones to you as a couple for creating your peaceful home together, then support one another to enforce them in a mutually agreed-upon manner.

CREATE A CONTINGENCY PLAN

Consider having a contingency plan for really bad days. Researcher and storyteller Brené Brown talks about the myth of fifty-fifty in relationships in one of her podcasts. She muses that each of us comes to the end of the day with our tanks empty, full, or somewhere in between. We often look to our coparents to make up for the amount we are depleted, so if you are running at 10%, you expect your partner to be at 90% to make up for your amount of drain. However, there are days where both of you are only functioning at 10% or 20%, and then what? This is the time to pull out your contingency plan. It just may be pizza and a movie night for the family, or some other low-maintenance evening plan that you can each count on for refueling both of you—or at least not further depleting your stores.

Staying Regulated in the Heat of the Moment

Attending to your overall well-being is critical for engaging with other humans, especially those who may need our help in finding their own calm and regulated state. We simply cannot give more from ourselves than we have to give. There are so many cliché statements I could make here. But when loving someone on the autism spectrum, we must remain centered more than ever. We may need deliberate self-soothing practices for the heat of the moment. This is when our own neurobiological systems spill over into our fight, flight, freeze, faint, or fawn mode. These are the moments when our hearts start racing, our palms are sweating, our self-talk is full of doom and gloom, and we yell or cry. These are very real moments that bring fear and worry to our days.

- An infant or baby may take longer to soothe, or it may seem like it will never happen.
- A child may hit or bite when frustrated or overwhelmed.
- A teen may withdraw to their room or get extremely defensive.
- An adult may yell or threaten with angry words over seemingly slight misunderstandings.

Any of these moments can put our own neurological systems in states of fight, flight, freeze or fawn. Our brains and bodies want to fight or run away. When we are trying to build a relationship with someone who has regulation needs, we often know cognitively that they are struggling, but our neurological systems may not agree. Therefore we need to care for ourselves first and foremost in these moments. We must find effective calming strategies to bring our own regulation back online so we can think clearly.

For us to be models for the other person while allowing them to "borrow" our regulation, we must be aware of our own personal state of regulation. By calming our own systems, research has shown that we can successfully calm another person's system as well. This occurs naturally through our body language, for example. By simply sitting down, we not only calm our own system, but we demonstrate to the other person that we are not a threat. By breathing deeply, reducing our own words, and calming our own bodies, we can actively model relaxation techniques.

For ideal guiding and connecting, we need to be present and regulated. In the moments when you start to become frustrated, notice how your own self-talk changes and how your own body reacts. Do you tense up? Do your palms sweat? Does your heart rate increase? While you are noticing your own body, observe your child's or the other person's bodily responses as well. Humans will naturally synchronize heart rates, breathing, and movements with one another when we are in close proximity and interacting!

Tragically, when your child or student is the source of your fear or potential pain due to aggressive behaviors, you have a huge mismatch with your own neurological system. Your child's or partner's behaviors may even evoke a post-traumatic stress response in you. This may tax your mental capacity for being in the moment and thinking through what to do next. I know I am asking for a lot, but you have the resiliency required. Before you approach that person with autism, take a deep breath and ensure your readiness. Again, I have placed some ideas for you in the back of this book. Experiment with what works for you to be grounded and ready when an escalated moment occurs.

I support a girl, age thirteen, who is gentle and kind at her core. I know this because she brings me flowers, she smiles, she is playful, and she hugs me goodbye. But when she is anxious or something unexpected happens, she can be one of the most aggressive people I have known. She switches on a dime. She will be curious and engaged and then suddenly attack by grabbing me and biting my head.

I have served her family for years and watched professional after professional try various behavioral approaches with her, with only minor success. It seemed I was watching her confidence wane with every failed attempt to help her. I was tired of seeing this amazing young person not feeling like she was seen for her worth. I insisted on meeting with her directly.

For the first few sessions, I had to work very hard at my own self-calm and grounding techniques even before she walked in the door. My heart would race, my breathing would become shallow, and my own self-talk was full of doubt. I knew that I needed to be there for her no matter what in order to connect with her. I practiced my deep breathing for the few minutes before her arrival. Then I practiced deep breathing during our session together. I kept my own words to an extreme minimum, and when things got scary, I grounded my feet and used my emergency behavioral strategies for everyone's safety.

As our weekly sessions progressed, she trusted me more and more. She no longer protested the drive to my office, and she stayed and engaged longer, telling me when she wished to go rather than launching into her routine of aggression and severe self-injury. Slowly but surely, we started engaging in social reciprocity, joint attention, and shared interactions during board games such as Mouse Trap and imaginary play with characters from her favorite shows—adding new characters and new voices.

CHAPTER 4

Presuming Competence

By holding the highest vision for your child when they cannot see it for themselves, you are lifting them up, elevating them and helping them to soar.
—Megan Koufos

In the autism field, we have gone in a very odd direction of assuming children and individuals with autism cannot learn on their own and need us neurotypicals to teach them everything they need to know. We have developed a full set of alternative parenting and guiding interventions just for autism. We have camps that compete and disagree about how to best guide individuals on the spectrum. One on side, we have interventions that follow a child's lead completely, and on the other side, we teach compliance and skill development.

I, too, thought for many years that autism took a completely different set of skills for teaching and guiding. I thought that individuals with autism needed us to teach each skill they were lacking. It was overwhelming to consider all of the skills that a human would need in their lives to be successful. The thought that a child would need every single skill methodically broken down and taught discretely seemed like an incredibly daunting task. I was up for the challenge due to my love and curiosity about those with autism, and so I was a behavior-based interventionist for years. And some research does show the efficacy of teaching skill development in this manner. That said, human behavior is incredibly complex and individualized, as you read in chapter 1. Social development is nuanced and often chaotic. To think that we have to basically create a human from the ground up by teaching them everything we know is a ridiculous goal. And it is incredibly disrespectful to the autistic individual.

In my work as a behavior-based interventionist, it seemed that much of the time, I was simply uncovering what a child already knew rather than specifically teaching them. I determined that once I made things clear and safe, they would demonstrate to me their true and natural learning. Individuals with autism are completely capable of learning and growing in their own unique and wonderful ways—they just need nurturing at times for balance, well-being, regulation, and social success. It is my professional opinion that when we meet children or individuals where they are in development, joining them with the understanding set forth in this book, we guide them to learn more robustly, more independently, and with their own personal agency. The alternative—teaching as if they can't learn on their own—is ableist. It is ridiculous to think that we as neurotypicals know everything and they are unable to learn on their own. When we teach rather than guide, we run the risk of individuals fighting and becoming "behavior challenges" or falling into prompt dependency that does not work for long-term independence.

I am tired of meeting teen after teen who has been on the compliance path too long. They are unable to make the transition to adulthood because of it. They are either angry, exhausted, or so prompt-dependent that they are unable to make decisions for themselves, let alone feel confident in their own abilities. It is essential to respect an individual's ability to learn with their own unique style. It is our job to guide them for better balance and to alleviate obstacles to that natural learning. The guidelines in this chapter for presuming competence are here to alleviate those obstacles and make way for each person's unique learning style.

Presuming competence and raising expectations of someone's capability is essential to respecting and connecting with them. Every individual, with or without autism, wishes to be respected, held to appropriate expectations, and challenged in ways that are manageable and attainable. With expectations too high, you run the risk of inducing anxiety in the person to perform to your standards. With expectations too low, you run the risk of a person assuming they are not capable of achieving more for themselves. Our aim is to find that zone where the person is challenged to new learning without being either overwhelmed or so underwhelmed that they shut down out of boredom. In autism, that zone can be narrow. The child, teen, or adult may shut down or become aggressive if we push too hard or if we do not push enough. When we push too hard, we reinforce feelings of failure while increasing anxiety. When we do not push enough, we give the message that we do not think they are capable. Our goal is for them to presume competence in themselves by finding manageable ways to be challenged. We cannot achieve that by undermining their ability or we are always going to come up short. We want to give the individual the sense that we believe in them and their ability to engage with us in their own unique way without being rushed or pushed aside.

Set Clear Boundaries

Presuming competence for someone with autism may mean setting clear behavior boundaries that are at the individual's age level. Just because they have autism doesn't mean that you pander to their disability or allow them to do things you would not otherwise allow them to do. Do not allow them to hurt you, for example. You may need to be even more clear and consistent about the behavioral (especially safety-related) boundaries and then deliberately support their flexibility in other aspects.

Children, both neurotypical and neurodiverse, need and thrive with behavioral boundaries. Without them, children do not feel the security of having a confident guide to keep them safe while they are exploring. Having clear, predetermined behavioral boundaries gives you as a guide more confidence in knowing your behavioral bottom lines while allowing the child to explore. This air of confidence with boundaries is extremely reassuring to children who feel comfort in structure and rules, as seen in autism.

Most people feel much more confident when they have a guide or coach sharing with them what the pitfalls might be while learning something new. When we are learning a new game or task, we need to know the boundaries that others have figured out before us through their own practice. These boundaries support our feelings of safety and confidence. Without them, we experience chaos and have very little to guide us as a starting point. We must have a balance. I have always liked the concept of having "boundaries that breathe," or boundaries that are set in a kind yet firm manner.

I once had a mother come to my office for the first time with deep scratches across her face. She was very friendly and kind as she sat down and shared about her sweet three-year-old child. She was looking for help for her son to be as successful as possible into adulthood. She wanted the relationship with her son that she felt was in jeopardy. She said nothing about challenging behaviors or the scratches on her face.

After letting her share her story, I asked, "Are those scratches from your son?" She replied that they were but tried to brush it off, stating that it was okay due to his autism. I shared with her what I am sharing with you here: just because he had autism did not give him permission to hurt her or others. She had been hurt when he was going for the fireplace and she had to move him away from it.

Putting what we now know about sensory and emotional flooding together with behavioral boundaries, we worked first on having alternatives for him to play with as well as the concept of "danger." She learned to be very clear about things in the house that were considered "danger" and which ones were safe for him to explore. She was quite adept at setting boundaries for her older neurotypical children, so when given permission to use the same tools and techniques behaviorally with her son with autism, she was quick to do so and was quite successful. Her son quickly stopped his aggression and became more settled with the clarity in behavioral boundaries provided.

Each family is different in which behavioral boundaries they wish to enforce. While dangerous situations are the most obvious ones to start enforcing boundaries right away, you may take some time to consider what other behavioral boundaries are important in your household. If you have a coparent, take some time to discuss what you feel together would create a more consistent home for you and for your child or children. If you are bothered by children or adults taking food from the kitchen into bedrooms or the living room, you may consider committing to a new household rule that food needs to stay in the kitchen or at the dining table, for example. If you have older children or teens, maybe you instill a rule that whomever cooks does not have to do dishes afterward, and those who do not cook do have to do the dishes afterwards.

Choose one to three household rules to target at a time. Do not try to tackle a huge list of targets all at once. You will be left frustrated and confused as to why enforcing them did not work. Select just one to three rules together with your coparent if possible or for yourself if you are a single parent. Write the rules down, and include how you will choose to enforce them. Be consistent, back each other up on the rules, and do not add another rule until the first ones are either mastered or you have determined other specific reasons that you are moving on from them.

If you need assistance with committing to and guiding behaviors, consider finding some support for yourself. There are often behavioral consultants available through social support services. They can help you decrease challenging behaviors and increase behaviors that are more beneficial for everyone. You can also collaborate with your child's team at school for consistency across settings, which will reduce any confusion for your child about specific behaviors.

Assuming Intent over Exact Words

As discussed in chapter 1, autism likely has motor challenges associated with it. The motor coordination it takes to form words is a phenomenal feat for anyone, in my opinion. It is rather astonishing that we can have a thought that then goes to the motor centers of our brains to form the intricate patterns in our mouths supported by our breath and lungs. So you can imagine that if something is different in the motor centers of the brain of autistic people, they may potentially say or do things they don't necessarily intend.

For example, a child who comes close to you and says a seemingly echoed phrase you have heard numerous times may be trying to convey that they need a hug or are wondering what you are doing. If we assume the intent of their bodies, we may hug, squeeze, or involve them in what we are doing. But if we assume the intent of only their exact words, we follow them down a rabbit hole by either engaging directly with what they are saying or telling them to stop repeating. We need to pay attention to the person's body language as much if not more than their verbal behavior. When someone approaches you with something that seems repetitive, for example, you can gaze to them inquisitively, touch them if they are comfortable with touch, then offer an alternative. You might invite them to help you in dinner preparations, if that is what you are doing at the time. They may just not have the motor planning to produce the words "I'm bored" or "Can I help?" They have also potentially well-developed habits of using particular phrases that are like slippery slopes—once they start down that sloped path, they slide into the phrase without being able to change direction to a new phrase. You can also presume competence by helping them shape their static request into more effective means of communication.

A client I have known for many years used to come into my office and ask, "What does it take to get out of this place?" which was a line from a Disney movie. (He had cataloged phrases from movies on his mother's phone and had over two hundred of them.) He was about ten years old, and he truly seemed to like to come to my office. He came in willingly, but as soon as he arrived, he would almost always use that phrase. His mother tried reassurance, sharing that "it isn't that bad to be with Barb," but he persisted.

I knew that he was also a very punctual person. He used his watch and was good about the starts and stops of classes and other things. I decided to assume he was asking me, "What time do we start and what time will we end?" I started responding to the unverbalized question, "What time do we start and end our session?" and writing down our start and stop times. Each time I responded in this manner, he calmed and joined me easily for the hour together.

Learned Helplessness

You have nothing to lose by presuming someone's competence and assuming they are capable of engaging with you. You have everything to lose by not having these expectations. By not presuming competence, you give the person the sense that they are not capable. This significantly contributes to what is called "learned helplessness." This is an individual's response to long-term overcompensations leading to feelings of inadequacy and dependency on others. This can happen when we:

- Talk down to them and keep them from stretching themselves to learn new things

- Avoid situations because we assume they are not able to join us instead of offering accommodations to make something manageable
- Fix problems for them before they even recognize that a problem exists
- Speak for them
- Speak about them without including them in the conversation
- Talk about their challenging behaviors in front of them

The opposite of learned helplessness would be "learned competence." This can happen when we:

- Speak in an age-appropriate manner
- Offer situations that may be challenging and manageable to build confidence
- Coach them to learn to fix their own challenges and advocate for themselves
- Allow them to speak for themselves (or communicate in other ways if verbal language is not as reliable for them)
- Include them in conversations about them, including decision-making

As I shared in chapter 1, autistic individuals often have an interesting mix of abilities. There are people who cannot verbally express themselves in sentences but can play complex piano pieces by memory or can draw whole city landscapes after flying over a city once. There are others who have repetitive behaviors and unreliable speech patterns but can communicate through letterboards or communication devices, demonstrating an intellect that is at or above their age level. And the majority of people with autism, like the rest of us, have not yet found their special interest or talent. All of us take our time exploring various topics throughout our lives to settle into a professional lane that feels comfortable for us. It may take a huge amount of trial and error to determine what challenges us without too much failure to keep us in that zone that still inspires us. It also takes the people surrounding us to encourage us without overwhelming us. Having someone who knows us well and who has high expectations of us can motivate us to achieve more than we ever thought we could.

Chores and Jobs

One cannot go wrong with high expectations while modifying the environment for ideal processing. You can go wrong by shooting too low. This is true for expectations regarding household chores and jobs.

As you know, due to sensory processing needs, children with autism may not push their own limitations or imitate their caregivers when they model certain behaviors, as children without autism do. This can lead us to assume that they are choosing not to challenge themselves or be helpful. The fact may be that they just need a nudge.

It may be a surprise or perhaps frustrating that a child who is not seemingly interested in helping you with household chores or jobs will rise to the occasion when specifically told that you need their help. Doing this in the early years can plant the seed for their feelings of self-worth, their confidence in being helpful, and their ability to give to others. I am a big fan of celebrating prosocial behaviors as soon and often as possible.

If you have a child who is seemingly more interested in in-animate objects, do not assume they are not interested in social engagement or participating in shared household responsibilities. Instead join them in very small and manageable ways so they can feel successful. Please refer to chapter 11, "Creating Partnerships," and appendix 6 for more partnering ideas. These are opportunities to offer structure during social interactions that can help a child feel safe enough to discover their own personal agency in relation to others.

When approaching your teen or adult about household chores, you may be met with typical teen resistance. If you speak to them in a singsong voice assuming they cannot understand you unless you speak that way, they will either ignore you, fight you, or respond accordingly—as if they are younger than they are. And if you assume high expectations and engage with them at their age level while modifying the environment for ideal processing, the same teen or adult will still either ignore you, fight you, or respond accordingly at their age level. As you can see, the person is still a teen or adult wanting independence. They may choose to ignore you or fight you while responding to your expectations. They will hear the message that you respect them, believe in them, and wish to engage with them. They will hear the message that you see them and the best version of them, making it much more likely that they will join you in sharing in house projects and other responsibilities over time. This confidence in them will be internalized, giving them their own strength and courage.

Control over One's Own Life

Along with presuming competence, also presume that development is typical in many realms, including the natural drive for control over one's life. The drive for control is especially apparent in the teen years, but many of us also know the adage of the "terrible twos." Fostering that drive for control is essential for natural learning. You can foster control while still guiding for balance by providing choices when and where appropriate.

Providing choices allows personal agency, while avoiding choices is a recipe for disaster for all humans, autistics included. And while many children who are neurotypical may demand their own control, individuals with autism may need you to offer it to them. Here are some ways you can provide choices to someone with autism:

- Give choices within nonchoices: allow control within situations where aspects may not be within their control. You could say, "We are going to the car. Do you want to bring the baseball or your book with you?"
- When transitioning, allow time for the person to finish what they are doing before shifting to your agenda. For example, if someone is focused on an episode of anime, allow them time to pause it themselves or finish the episode before demanding transition.
- If they need or want to move or "stim" while learning or engaging, allow them to do so. Only provide or teach alternatives when the movements get in the way of learning for that person or if their behaviors are unsafe.

Assume They Hear Everything You Say

The more I learn, research, and understand about autism, the more I am convinced that there is a neurological difference affecting the motor centers of the brain, as described in chapter 1. It has been demonstrated that infants who later develop autism take longer to disengage their attention from one stimulus to another. Now imagine if you were learning language with that time delay occurring. We learn language through what is called "joint attention." When we are looking at something and it is labeled at the same time, we learn that label. But what if your eyes and body could not coordinate properly to engage with others while gazing at objects? Your interactions would be asynchronous versus synchronous, and the world would be a pretty confusing place. Learning how to prioritize your attention would have a whole new meaning if you were primarily trying to have your observations match what your body could or couldn't do.

The motor centers of the brain are also responsible for initiating and coordinating the intricate movements required for speech. If autism indeed involves motor centers in the brain, it could mean that someone very well might understand everything said to them (or about them), but they may not be able to respond or engage verbally. They may struggle with the coordination of motor movements required to make their body and words adequately convey their thoughts.

When I observe a person with autism saying something that does not seem to make sense in the situation, I try to listen to their body language instead. They may not be able to communicate with you verbally, but that does not mean they are not listening and understanding. Their words may not match what they are trying to say. Presuming competence means that you assume they are hearing and processing everything you are saying.

There are two types of the speech pattern we call "echolalia." One refers to an immediate repeating back of what someone has said or just the last word. The other type is commonly referred to as delayed echolalia, when someone uses words or phrases that they have heard in the past to convey their thoughts. Someone might use a line from a movie or a scripted phrase like "I want milk" to indicate they want something, from a cookie to a snuggle.

A young adult whom I feel lucky to meet with twice a month engages in almost constant verbal loops or echoed statements. He also engages in ritualistic movements, like straightening items around him from shoes to clothes to books. At times he may be looking away and seemingly not engaged.

When his letterboard is in front of him, his inner voice comes to life. He straightens up, uses his pointer finger to touch each letter on the board, and communicates using words like any other adult. His words are full of emotion and swears, conveying his thoughts in a very age-appropriate manner. He can share with me and others how unfair it is that his sister and peers get to go out and be independent. He shares how angry he is that he is so reliant on others. He shares what helps him stay regulated and what makes him more frustrated—which happens to be when others are frustrated with him or do not honor or understand him. He has his own blog that explores and demands social justice and denounces ableism. He and others like him need to be heard and respected for what they have to say.

Another young adult I serve and have known for years is completely nonverbal. I have not heard any words from him in his twenty years. While he is very quiet, he is also a very compliant and observant person. He becomes agitated when he hears a dog barking in the distance and will become rigid and still when being asked to do something he does not want to do. He uses two fingers to tap his chin to answer "yes," especially to food he is being offered. This seems a variation of the sign for "eat" that he learned many years ago. He has had numerous evaluations to determine alternatives for communication for him, with at least one stating how ready and able he is to use applications via his iPad. He would need extensive support, including training to those around him on a daily basis, as everyone would basically be learning a new language. Sadly, insurance and costs have held the family back from being able to pursue this avenue for him.

In my sessions, I share age-appropriate music and spell out the band names for him either in writing or on a letterboard I have in my office. As I read articles about the bands to him, his engagement and attention are always fully present. I choose to presume competence with him. I choose to presume that he is hearing what I have to say, but his motor systems are not functioning properly enough for him to show me that understanding past his rapt attention. I tell him that I think he may be having trouble moving his body. When I say this, he smiles and gazes to me seemingly in affirmation. To assume he is simply incapable of understanding is to discount his thoughts, his feelings, and his personal agency.

"Letterboards" refer to plastic or paper displays of the alphabet. The person can use the board to point to letters that form words and sentences. The beauty of a letterboard is that there are no preconceived ideas presented as to what the person will say, as you see with many of the other assistive communication devices and systems out there. It is much more open-ended to bring out the "voice" of the individual using it.

Use Age-Appropriate Wording

We have discussed here how challenging it may be for people with autism to shift their attention. Through my experiences and research, I believe that motor planning is somewhere at the root of autism. People who are nonverbal may not have delays in their thinking (and receptive language) but have great difficulty getting those thoughts out to the world in the form of words.

Imagine for a moment a young child who has difficulty motorically shifting their attention from one stimulus to another. They have subsequently missed opportunities for the social reciprocity with others that teaches us so much about ourselves and the world. This would mean that the person was potentially not cognitively delayed until they missed so many opportunities to develop and grow that they started to fall more and more behind. For more information on attention shifting and infant studies, please refer to chapter 1, "The Cascade Effect."

Now imagine if in the smaller day-to-day moments, we assumed the person was cognitively engaged but was having difficulties with motor coordination and shifting of attention. We keep high expectations and presume competence. We would then speak to the person at their age level, but we'd also simplify our wording without talking down to them, and we would slow down to allow processing time.

Now imagine if in those same smaller day-to-day moments, we assumed cognitive delay and disinterest. We would then speak to the person by disregarding their age-appropriate needs or wants, using baby talk or talking down to them, and providing inadequate challenges for learning. To me this is unacceptable. When we disregard age-appropriate needs and wants, talk down to people, and provide inadequate learning challenges, we inadvertently thwart that person's feelings of confidence. We promote learned helplessness and drive prompt dependency on others.

In order to presume intent by supporting the person's feelings of competency, we use the person's chronological age as a guideline. We speak to and engage the individual as we would anyone of that person's same age. We modify our wording and provide more processing time. We talk about things that most people their age would be interested in and explore those interests with them. This may take experimentation to figure out. Looking to more age-appropriate activities may help you determine what to present. There are more activities on such sites as Pinterest than one could ever imagine.

Upping the Ante

I frequently support parents and professionals in upping the ante when an individual has challenging behaviors. This may seem counterintuitive if you are worried that you may be overwhelming a person. It may come as a surprise that challenging behaviors crop up when an individual is underwhelmed as well. If we think about what is known as the "zone of proximal development," which I mentioned in chapter 2, we are aiming for that zone in which they are optimally able to learn. If we are interacting above their ability, we overwhelm a person, and if we go below their ability, we bore them or underwhelm them.

I once worked with a nonverbal, extremely impulsive eight-year-old boy who had only ever been offered sensory and developmentally young toys. He would attempt to grab or manipulate things in his environment that were metal, like locks and jewelry. I suggested that his parents up the ante for what they offered in his play and exploration. I suspected that he was being offered things that were underwhelming while noticing things in his environment that were intriguing—but being denied access. I think they thought I was crazy when I suggested that his father bring out a real drill and support him in screwing real screws into a piece of wood in the backyard. I wish you could see this kid's face light up and his calm, focused intrigue when his father engaged him in this way. It was magical.

I have also had teens light up when I or others offered edgy and angsty music that is typical for their age. I have had adults rise to the occasion to join in budgeting discussions for their family. And I once had a teen who was literally tearing up the family home—terrifying his parents and brother—but when offered the opportunity to make a family meal each week and take on more responsibility for himself, his behaviors reduced dramatically.

Honoring Special Interests

Sometimes honoring a person's special interests or "splinter skills" requires us to raise expectations and presume competence too. We may push the special interests aside, thinking they are simply a symptom of autism. But these special interests, as Dr. Temple Grandin and Dr. Stephen Shore guide us to consider, may be a window into the person's future occupation.

Determining what your child's or partner's special interests are, while being creative with them, may be one of the most respectful things you can do for them. Listening to, being curious about, and raising your expectations about a person's interests can be key to guiding them in life and career choices. Exploring their special interests will help you better understand how their brain processes while seeing their strengths and their passions. As you will see in chapter 9, "Getting Curious," it is when we get curious that we can ideally engage someone for lifelong learning and connection.

Talk About Emotions—in Moderation

When determining how to presume competence with teens and adults, you may have to consider your options a bit differently. Teens and adults need more sophisticated supports that require your authentic respect for their personalities, emotions, sexuality, fear of failure, and feelings of loneliness. Each one of us, autistics included, are either introverts, extroverts, or somewhere in between. We all experience emotions, and some of us are more intuitive than others. For many people on the autism spectrum, emotions are felt more deeply and more intensely while also in a less organized manner. This leads to immense overwhelm emotionally. Others may need support in understanding the complexity of feeling multiple emotions at once, or that our intellect may understand something but our emotions sometimes do not—causing depression, loneliness, or simply a confusing disconnect.

When we ignore that someone is having intense and overwhelming emotional responses, we disregard them and move toward demanding compliance. The emotional life of that individual is then pushed aside. This gives the individual the message that either emotions are not important or that *their* emotions are not important. Either way, this is not an adequate reflection of humanity that helps the individual in being successful in relationships.

Please use emotional words with teens and adults with autism. Do not shy away from them because they are complex or confusing. This only makes it worse. Validate regularly using emotion words. Some individuals may balk at this at first, as they may have built up defensive habits. Go slow and make it manageable. Stay in the zone of proximal development and the window of tolerance so that best learning and integration can happen for that individual and for you.

Celebrate the Natural Drive for Independence

Everyone desires control and independence in their lives. Teens start to push away from their parents and caregivers in a natural progression toward adulthood. You can support this drive without thwarting it by ensuring they have adequate choices and control over their lives.

For teens and adults living at home, consider slowly and deliberately adding household chores and responsibilities. You might determine a schedule for them to make dinner once per week. To support this happening, you may start by having them partner with you (find more on partnering in chapter 11) in the kitchen in small doses before they are completely on their own. You may also consider having them start to "pay rent" when they turn eighteen years old. This may not look like we commonly imagine; it may take on different forms. The person may "pay rent" by taking on increasing responsibilities in the home that you outline visually for them (there's more in chapter 5, "Not Relying on Auditory Processing"). I recently had a family offer choices for how their son could pay rent in a list format with monetary amounts next to each item: cooking for family = $20; taking out the garbage = $5. Their son was able to choose (feeling personal agency) which of the items he wished to do each month to repay the rent he owed.

Once a person with autism turns eighteen, they may be eligible for adult services and disability benefits. Please see a financial and life-planning professional for more information.

In addition to tasks, chores, and responsibilities, raise your expectations with teens and adults for conversations and connections that feel pleasant rather than just talking when you need or want something from them. It is very common for teens and adults to retreat to their rooms, stop coming out for dinnertime, and become completely nocturnal just to avoid parents or guides who reinforce their feelings of incompetency. We must raise our expectations that through celebrating them, their thoughts, and their feelings, we can also raise their confidence, which will lead to their greater independence. It is not a lack of ability or skill development that's typically holding them back. It is their lack of confidence.

Choose to engage in the autistic person's special interests so they feel seen and heard. Even if the interests are not in your wheelhouse, listen and observe—you may learn something. Speak with fewer and more concrete words while giving more processing time. And, last but not least, let them surprise you with their unique and wonderful ideas.

Part I

Are You Seeing Autism?

By applying the information you glean from this book, you are one step closer to seeing autism. And by seeing autism, you will be better equipped to connect with someone on the spectrum. Seeing them may be the only intervention that is necessary.

What stood out to you in this section?
What would you like to remember?

The Cascade Effect

Sensory and
Emotional Flooding

Your Own Self-Care
and Well-Being

Presuming Competence

PART II

CONNECT

Autistic individuals thrive on connection just like all human beings. The key is to see and engage with their unique way of processing information.

CHAPTER 5

Not Relying on Auditory Processing

English is my second language. Autism is my first.
—Dani Bowman

I do not consider this just another autism book, so here I will not be sharing pictures or selling you on copywritten visual materials that you should be using with your child, friend, or partner with autism. Instead I ask you to consider offering alternative modes of communication rather than relying on auditory processing.

Most people with autism can seem to be listening to your words and even agree to what you say—but they may not have digested any of it. You may share the schedule of the day verbally or have a whole conversation about how to remedy a situation. But then the person seems to "forget" the words that were only spoken aloud. When someone is relying not on auditory processing but other inputs, they are keenly observing you and the environment around them. We need to consider what our body, our posture, and our environment are conveying, as these are often stronger modes for someone on the autism spectrum. They may be struggling to interpret the sheer magnitude of messages of each detail they see. To combat this sensory flood, we must reduce the input, get quiet, and get clear.

Relying on Visual Information

Do you remember swimming as a kid and listening to what the world sounded like while you were underwater? I do. It takes me back to my neighborhood community pool with my friends. I remember the muffled voices and the distant squeal of the whistle being blown to tell us it was time to get out for a break. I now wonder if this muffled audio from my memory may be similar to how people with autism experience sound. The sounds may be muffled, but you can still hear them. You can't really tell which direction the sounds are coming from. You can't make out the specifics of what people are saying. Now imagine if you experienced sound like that all of the time. You would have to rely on the visual information around you to determine where the sound was coming from and what was expected of you.

Dr. Temple Grandin is an autistic woman who speaks publicly about her autism and her work in designing livestock equipment. She has written several books on the subject of autism, all of which I recommend highly. As she describes it, "My hearing is like having a hearing aid with the volume control stuck on 'super loud.' It is like an open microphone that picks up everything. I have two choices: turn the mike on and get deluged with sound, or shut it off. Mother reported that sometimes I acted like I was deaf. Hearing tests indicated that my hearing was normal. I can't modulate incoming auditory stimulation" (Grandin 1992).

Many autistic adults have mentioned to me that they are unable to filter or prioritize sounds that are coming in around them. A car horn may sound as if it is in the immediate vicinity when it is actually outside on the street. A fan or an overhead light may have a buzzing sound that comes in at the same auditory level as someone's voice. The person may be in one of two states: absolute overwhelm trying to figure out which of the equal-decibel sounds is most important, or completely tuned out or shut down. The person might give up or give in to the cacophony of sound and go inward to his or her own thoughts as a defense mechanism.

I have watched my own partner in a variety of settings, including a busy local bar full of TVs, conversations, and happy hoopla. He is miserable in these types of settings. He becomes quiet, distant, and grumpy. I was so frustrated at first, since I do like to be social and check out the local eateries. Over time, I learned he is not antisocial; he cannot filter the noise. There is no hope of having a conversation when he is in this state.

We have developed strategies that work, like finding quieter locations or sitting at the bar, where it is often less busy and we can sit next to each other, making it easier to hear one another. We also go to predictable locations where we know and like the menu, the wait staff, and the seating arrangements. Having at least some of the variables be predictable seems to help when other aspects cannot be controlled.

With his own family (he has many siblings), he can be active, engaged, and incredibly social. But as you might suspect, those sounds and that manner of being social may feel predictable and safe when an unpredictably noisy and crowded local restaurant or bar does not.

Auditory Processing Challenges

Most people on the autism spectrum also have diagnosable auditory processing challenges. The data is very unreliable at this point, stating that it affects 30% to 90% of those with autism. I can comfortably say that I have not met someone with autism in my thirty-plus-year career who did not process sound differently. I can only imagine how hard it would be to have to constantly struggle with filtering or prioritizing what I am hearing.

I have had clients who seem not to hear; in fact, it is commonly the first concern young parents have for their children who later develop autism. I have several clients who will get distracted by the way a word or phrase sounds. It seems to tickle their funny bone or trigger a particular memory as if it were happening again in that new moment.

One of my young adult clients who I have known for many years will get a distant look after I have said something that rhymes or a word that sounds funny to him. He will go as far to extrapolate as to where he might use the word or phrase again later that will be even funnier.

Many years ago, we shared a hilarious moment when I heard what I called a "booming car" outside blaring its radio. And more recently, when we were talking about Asperger's syndrome, he got that look and had the teenage response about the word, hearing it as "ass-burger." He thought it was so funny and simply could not get back to the discussion at hand until we played it out. We now have a running joke about ordering an "ass-burger" at the local burger joint and seeing what they do!

I'm still unsure why "Joe's (insert any word)" makes him laugh so deeply or how saying something that then rhymes with Joe, like "Oh no, Joe!" makes him laugh even harder.

Additionally, many years ago I was a group home parent and served a young man who seemed to recognize and connect with people using singsong phrases unique to each individual. He would greet a co-group-home parent with a Grateful Dead version of "Hey, Bo Diddley dee," for example. I felt such privilege when I received my unique phrase. I knew then that I had gained his trust and connection.

He liked to play with the thin green plastic strapping that goes around packages like large boxes of produce. He would wiggle it in front of his eyes and manipulate it with his fingers. One day I pretended to grab it from him playfully, saying, "Gimme that" in a singsong tone. I can hear it to this day. (If you say it out loud, emphasize and elongate the "GIMMeeeee thaaaaaat!") He would laugh and repeat the phrase. And from that day on, it was how we greeted each other. Before I even entered the door, he'd mimic my voice, saying "Gimme that!" He would smile and giggle that same giggle every time, which made me smile and giggle in return.

As mentioned in chapter 4, some individuals with autism engage in a verbal behavior called "echolalia." They echo back what they have heard.

Children and adults with immediate echolalia repeat back what you have said verbatim or the last word you have said. When you say, "Do you want this?" they may say, "Do you want this" rather than yes or no. Consider immediate echolalia as an indication to slow down and go quiet. It's an indication that verbal communication is not working. Use other ways of communicating rather than just relying on them hearing your spoken words. You may stop talking all together and offer two visual or concrete choices in your hands while making it very clear that you are asking them to pick one, for example.

Other individuals have what is called "delayed echolalia," which is when they take phrases others have said, often from movies, and use them in different situations and interactions with others. The amount of work this must take for an individual to learn verbal language in this way astounds me. Can you imagine learning whole phrases to mean things rather than single labels?

I had one client who had delayed echolalia. He might say, "This iceberg life is unbearable," (which I believe was from the animated movie) when he was cold and needed a jacket. If you go with his exact words, the people supporting him might go into a whirlwind of responding with things like, "We aren't on an iceberg. We are at home," or "Are you thinking of polar bears? Roar!" or worst yet, "We can't watch that movie right now." Goodness, the confusion that could ensue for that person learning language and for those around him to learn this language too! Imagine if the person was saying this phrase: "This iceberg life is unbearable when I don't have my warm coat," when they are trying to make a statement that they feel warm or cozy. This would make social development almost impossible, as the child is conceivably very misunderstood. The social engagement they so desperately need and want takes a back seat as the individual tries to make sense of the world around them.

It is imperative to avoid the use of only verbal and auditory information with someone with autism. Providing visual information to someone who struggles with processing auditory information helps understanding and connection considerably. It creates an environment where you know you are thinking about the same thing!

In workshops it is common for me to start talking about "visual information" and for my audiences to start imagining that I am referring to the laminated, colored line drawings you see in therapy settings and classrooms. My recommendations surrounding visuals are *much* more immediate and user-friendly than just these colored line drawings or photos. The visual information we soak in is so much greater than these, and autistic individuals often become excellent at navigating the details. We need to catch up to how they see the world in order to engage successfully.

Pay Attention to Your Body Language

When I talk about visual information, again, I am not talking about colored line drawings but a much wider array of visual information. For one, consider how one's body language can visually support or distract from your message. If you say "let's go" while sitting down and looking relaxed, someone with autism may assume you are not ready to go and may even start doing something else. If you have a book in your hand while telling a child it's time for lunch or a bath, they may be confused and protest before you understand that your words and body language did not match. The person with autism took your body language, which is visual information, over your words to understand the situation. You are left wondering why your child reacted that way. You may even try talking louder or using more words to try to alleviate the confusion—only making it worse.

Body language can calm and redirect or conversely can stress and overwhelm. We are learning more and more every day about how our brains and bodies work together. For example, you can use your body to both calm and redirect others by sitting down (or getting low) to reduce the individual's fight-or-flight response. Or you can guide attention by blocking access to things you are not wishing for someone to choose while directing attention to those options that are acceptable.

If someone processes auditory information differently or simply less reliably than visual information, they may reference your body positioning over your words, so make it count. Standing up versus sitting down in different settings can have very different messages. For example, if you stand over someone, it can be intimidating. You may get a very instinctual response to fight or flee from you. Standing too close to someone can give opposite messages: you are romantically interested in someone or trying to intimidate them. Pointing to something while saying another thing can be confusing. Ensuring your gestures and words match will help immensely when interacting with someone with autism and/or auditory processing needs.

I know a seven-year-old boy with autism who is non-verbal, puts almost everything he can find in his mouth, and is guided minute by minute by one of his parents or his caregivers. His family was trying to allow him to be more independent rather than them having to physically redirect his hands, arms, and feet from grabbing, kicking, or falling to the floor when they transitioned between rooms of their home. He would start out well and then see an empty room or the water dispenser on the refrigerator. He'd slip into the room or to that dispenser with such ease and swiftness it made your head spin!

But when the adults started going silent and simply using their body and an outstretched, guiding arm as he walked past rooms instead of just trying to stop his flailing arms, he started being able to walk from one room to another without escaping. The outstretched arms guiding him down the hallway helped him keep the goal in mind. His parents and caregivers could let go of him and allow him to walk under his own volition by simply blocking off the distractions with their body and gestures.

Consider Levels of Representation

It is critical to consider the person's ability to receive the visual information you present. In the field of autism, while we're well-intentioned, we tend to go straight for preprinted options like drawings or photos to represent things we are trying to communicate. The person may not be ready to comprehend the information provided in that format. You can and should consider the level of representation they understand best.

In human development, we have to learn that symbols, both written and verbal, can represent objects and activities. Developmentally we must learn that a physical, 3-D, red ball is a ball every time we see it, for example. Next we learn that a photo of a red ball also represents a ball. Then a colored line drawing can represent the ball, and then a black-and-white drawing of a ball represents a ball. Last but not least, we learn to infer that written words can also represent objects and even activities. If we start out with the colored line drawings, we are asking for the person to potentially make a developmental leap. If we are deliberate and start with their developmental level of representation, we are working within their ideal comprehension.

You can find out what developmental level the individual you are supporting understands best by consulting a speech language specialist. You can also offer the visual options in a developmental sequence and experiment with which seems to work best for your child or partner. I am presenting them in developmental order here with suggestions of how you might use them.

3-D OBJECTS

Actual 3-D objects can be incredibly helpful for a child struggling with auditory processing. Having a 3-D object to support that joint attention will also support your partner's optimal understanding.

When you are talking or communicating about something, consider having an object related to what you are sharing. If you are talking about food, have the food you are talking about there in front of the two of you. If you are talking about basketball, have a basketball with you. Consider gathering physical souvenirs from trips you take so you can talk about them later. A rock from a riverbed you enjoyed while camping can bring the experience and memories to life again. An autumn leaf collected on a walk earlier in the day can aid in your remembering the walk later and sharing it with those who did not go with you.

Having an item from the location you are going to together can also help tremendously in a shared understanding of your destination, significantly reducing stress of the transition. If you wish to change their diaper, for example, bring the diaper to them. If you wish to have them help you in the garden, bring gardening gloves or a bucket with you to invite them to join you. Using 3-D objects to transition can also help you and the child keep the goal destination in mind to reduce the possibility of getting distracted along the way.

Some other ideas for sharing via 3-D objects include the following:

- Offer a spatula to someone when you would like their help in the kitchen.
- Hand a clean towel to someone you wish to join you to dry dishes, fold laundry, or put these items away.
- Hand a child a backpack when it is time to head out to the car.
- Give someone a piece of a puzzle you wish to do together in the other room.
- Offer someone a cup if you wish to know if they are thirsty.
- Bring a toothbrush to someone when it is time to start the bedtime routine.

PHOTOS

The next level of representation is photos. Some people may need support at first in pairing the objects with the photos to help them transition to this the higher level. Some may already understand this level of representation, as it is prevalent in many cultures. We see photos of food, toys, and clothing in advertisements. We readily take photos and videos of each other and our families to send to loved ones and post on social media.

You can use photos for transitioning, celebrating, or simply sharing a story. Joining your partner where they are physically and then offering a photo to share where they are going next can help them understand. Some parents, for example, find it helpful to have photos of different rooms in their house to use when helping their child transition from one room to another. Other families find it helpful to have photos of people pinned up on a wall to display who their partner may see throughout the day (e.g., teachers, parents, grandparents, or caregivers). Sharing photos for transitioning between events or activities can ease anxiety about what is happening next or later in the day, week, or even the month. Photos on calendars, for example, can help with understanding that an anticipated event is coming but is days or months away.

Photos can also be used to celebrate events or achievements. Now that we use our phones as cameras, we can take pictures of everyday events and celebrate them. A child who learns to put on their own socks can share a photo or video with others, who can then celebrate with them. An adult who shaved by themselves might share before and after photos with somebody to celebrate their newfound skill and independence. Or you might start a collection of photos of times when the person with autism has been especially brave or tried something new. Photos can help solidify memories, emotions, and confidence.

A little girl with whom I worked collected photos of times when she was brave. She had photos of the new foods and new activities she tried. She and her family called her collection her "Brave Book." Whenever she was feeling anxious about trying something she had never tried before, she and her family would sit down together and review the Brave Book, celebrating and reinforcing the moments in her life where she was once nervous and ended up feeling brave.

Photos can also be helpful for calling up emotions associated with memories. You can see the smiles on people's faces when they are happy, proud, or think something is funny, leading to re-experiencing the moment. Using photos at the dinner table can also bring conversations to life. Sometimes dinner can be all about eating and lasts all of five or ten minutes while the food is wolfed down. By bringing photos to the table, maybe one or two can spark memories, ensuring a joint reference point for the conversation for everyone, including the person on the autism spectrum. It encourages shared attention versus distraction or the hyper-focus solely on eating.

COLORED LINE DRAWINGS

Admittedly, I was the self-proclaimed queen of Velcro and colored line drawings in my classroom. I had them up for each student to demonstrate their schedules for the day. I had them at the snack table to offer choices of snack foods. I had them in sequences for play and even how to greet a friend. I had them on a lanyard for helping kids know what I was asking of them. If they needed to use the toilet or have a break, I had the colored line drawing at the ready. They can be quite helpful.

It commonly happened, though, that we did not seem to have that exact laminated Velcroed colored line drawing we needed in the most crucial situations or the most ideal learning engagements. Even though I had hundreds (if not thousands) of these laminated visuals, time and time again I did not have the one I needed. Then I went into private practice, where I tried to support parents in using these by getting them from their education teams. But again, and even worse, they never had the one they needed at the most crucial moments—not to mention the cost of the professional's time, plus all of that ink, lamination, and Velcro. I learned through these experiences that while prefabricated line drawings in that form were helpful, they did not have the usability necessary for the complexity of real life.

DRAWING IN BLANK NOTEBOOKS

I decided to experiment with being much more low-tech in my support of parents in their homes and communities. There are amazing benefits to parents learning the why behind the use of visuals in the form of drawing to gain joint understanding between them and their child on the spectrum. When we start with blank notebooks or sticky pads and then draw alongside the person with whom we are communicating, the understanding can seem like magic.

Instead of thinking the drawing has to be perfect or even great, we must focus on the fact that through guiding joint attention to the drawing, individuals with autism often have excellent memories and will remember what the drawing represents. Do not worry if your drawing skills are poor. Just make sure you have joint attention with the person (their attention is on you as well as the visual representation) while you are drawing. Stick figures are just fine.

Some examples of when you might use drawing for visual support are as follows:

- Routines, such as bedtime or morning routines to increase independence
- Checklists for homework, chores, daily hygiene
- Social sequences, like how to greet peers or ask what they may be thinking about
- Behavioral boundaries, like using a "1st → then" format
- Celebrations of things you are proud they have done for later review

WRITTEN WORDS

Some individuals with autism are quite adept at decoding words very early. Words are fairly concrete and many rarely change. From street signs to favorite logos, they are static and common in our lives. Books are predictable and concrete, some more than others. Written words may be particularly helpful for those on the autism spectrum. They may be able to read simple, concrete words well before you might expect due their attention to the detailed visual information surrounding them.

Similar to the drawings, you can use written words for the same and more:

Routines

Checklists

Social sequences

First → then expectations

Celebrations

Working out problems

A mother I knew well decided to start writing her four-year-old son little notes on sticky pads and placing them around the house. She was struggling with the fact that he was sneaking time on his electronic device. She started putting notes up in the house to remind him: "dinner then iPad." This developed into: "dinner at 5pm then iPad at 6pm."

She found that while he had been getting quite anxious and even aggressive when the information was provided verbally, she could take out a piece of paper, go silent, and share information that would calm him quickly. She extended the notes to offer little positives, like "Thank you for helping make dinner" and simply, "I love you."

His agitation eased across his days as his mom had found a way to communicate with him more effectively simply through the use of written words. She was able to successfully find a healthy balance of positive affirmations that are such a sweet aspect of parenting with the cues and directives so common for autism parenting.

Keep It Simple and Keep It Handy

Keep the photos, drawings, or written words simple. Just as you will read in chapter 7, "Decluttering the Environment," you will need to address and potentially simplify visual information. Use a photo, draw, or write only the essentials, especially when you first start. A schedule should only be one to two words for each activity. For example: get dressed → breakfast → car → school → play → chores → dinner, and so on. Breaking up the schedule into chunks so that it is not visually overwhelming at one time can also be helpful. So instead of having the full day outlined, you may offer the steps just until one major transition: get dressed→ breakfast→ car→ school. Then you can begin another schedule that outlines what happens after school: school→ play → chores→ dinner, and so on.

Like I mentioned above, when I first started using visual supports for people on the autism spectrum, I used pre-created and laminated colored line drawings almost exclusively. I learned through the years, though, to view visual supports in a much more holistic way. Now I use them to support joint attention to what is next or what I want to highlight.

The use of concrete visual information, including body language, photos, drawings, or written words, is critical to support the joint attention and subsequent understanding between you. It cannot be utilized only when we want them to do something. By also ensuring visual supports for a back-and-forth engagement, we raise our expectations and presume their competence in sharing their ideas as well. For example, offering a blank notebook and drawing a couple of stick figures or simple words will bring both parties' attention together. Then sliding the notebook toward the autistic person for idea sharing opens the door for their understanding that you want to hear what they have to say as well.

A client who I have had for many years does not use verbal communication as his primary mode. He has been resistant to the continued use of the colored line drawings used in school for his own communication. A couple of years ago, based on my recommendation, his mother started placing a blank notebook between them at their dinner table. She would take the notebook out each evening and share a couple of things that had happened that day in rough drawings or words. She would then leave the book open with the pen oriented toward her son. She did this repeatedly over several weeks, and one day he picked up the pen and started writing his own words. The conversations between them came to life slowly via this simple blank notebook.

Be sure to find a balance between the things you want to them to do and the things they want to do. For example, consider putting screen time or talking about favorite subjects on their visual schedule. And bring the written word into your play together. You could say "fast" and "slow" when playing together with race cars, or "sleep" and "awake" when pretending to be asleep then awake together while playing. Dr. Connie Kasari's research out of UCLA demonstrates that when we augment our verbal words with visual representations in play, children become increasingly verbal.

The client whose mother uses the blank notebook at mealtimes started requesting that things be written and would suggest things be shared in that manner. Within a matter of months, he had seemed to truly grasp the value of the written word for him to use as well. He started texting his brothers and father on his phone, for example.

Fast-forward to an email I received from this family just the other day. My client had independently written down what was wrong with his computer prior to bringing it into a shop to be fixed, with his mother there as backup. When they got to the shop, he handed the written note to the repair person. The repair person in turn wrote down the appointment time and date for picking it up. My client took the paper, put it in his own pocket (rather than relying on his mother), and remembered the time and date on his own. When they returned, the computer was repaired according to his note. He had one of his first independent exchanges with a community business, and we suspect it was only the beginning.

Social Stories

Social stories are a common example of visual supports used in the autism community, but many use them incorrectly. They were originally developed by a woman named Carol Gray to guide individuals through social situations that they were seeming to misunderstand or needed more information.

Social stories are a way to help someone process a given situation and to provide more information that the autistic person may not have been aware of. For example, a person may have posted something political to their social media site and gotten a confusing laughing emoji as a comment on the post. The person may have been subsequently upset and confused as to whether this person was laughing at them or the post—either way felt confusing. A social story should be cocreated with that person explaining the social nuances that may not have been understood. In this case, the social story may have shared more details as to why someone may post emojis or the various meanings of them. It might just as easily be a social story about how others on your social media accounts may have very different ideas about politics and how to handle that dynamic. This is why they are constructed together—so that the story is tailored to the personal needs of the person for whom it is written.

The official social story use, as directed by Carol Gray, has specific guidelines to follow to keep you from being too preachy or judgmental. They are always meant to be very personal to the individual and they are meant to be light, informational, positive, and forward thinking. The story is also designed to be reviewed regularly when similar situations arise or simply when the person wishes to think about the scenario. Some people have three-ring binders, for example, full of social stories to reference as they encounter various social situations.

Spotlighting One's Unique Contributions

I have used letterboards and sentence starters to help my clients share their unique thoughts. It is common for people who are less verbal to be quite prompt-dependent and allow others to speak for them. This can cause someone to not even realize that they have their own thoughts.

It is always my goal within each session with someone with autism to ensure that they know they have a voice with me. Sometimes I will help them own and share their unique contributions by typing side by side on a computer. We're having a conversation in typed form—physically passing the laptop back and forth. At first they may protest lightly, so I simply say something like, "I can't speak for you," or "You have great ideas." Other times I may bolster a person's unique contributions by taking turns on a whiteboard drawing pictures.

Cocreating stories and drawings rather than each having your own is an excellent way to support someone in understanding their impact on you and your collaborations. You will read more about this later in chapter 11. Here is a sneak peek as it relates to the use of visuals.

A young man who I meet with weekly is able to use a fill-in-the-blanks game to communicate his thinking with me, as he is not typically able to do so verbally. We started years ago with this game to help him realize that he could have something in his thoughts that I did not know. To represent that fact, we would always start our sessions with this game.

The game is similar to *Wheel of Fortune*, where one person draws lines to indicate each letter of a word or phrase. The other person must then guess letters to fill in each space. At first, he would say the word he was going to use for his turn, and I would guide him to write it down for himself where I couldn't see it rather than saying it out loud. Then we quickly moved to his not needing to write it down; he knew to keep it silently in his thoughts.

Fast-forward a few years, and in our first Zoom session online after the start of the COVID-19 pandemic, he was super motivated to write an elaborate set of blanks for me to guess the letters. It was a question—a full sentence, complete with the question mark at the end. It ended up being, "When will coronavirus be off?" Mind you, this is a man who is not able to ask questions verbally, and no one even knew he was curious about the pandemic. As a result we ended up watching a short informational video on the virus, which he then requested we watch three times before announcing he was finished.

Without this fill-in-the-blanks game routine of his sharing his own unique thoughts with me through writing, I would not have discovered his age-appropriate curiosity about the world crisis, nor would I have then shared more in-depth information. Information can be calming. It is the uncertainty and the unknown that is the most unsettling for all of us.

Making Decisions

I provide choices to autistic individuals in a format I call the "Sun Diagram." It looks like a sun where the center represents an issue you are trying to solve and each of the rays out to the sides of the sun represents the choices or options available. I specifically offer them in the circular manner so that they do not think that it is a list of to-do items or a schedule where they need to do each item in order. Offering choices in this circle format can help someone understand visually that each item is a choice.

Individuals with autism often also have difficulty with thinking about a subject from multiple angles, or what we call dynamic thinking. If there is an issue, an autistic individual may state, think, and determine that there is only one solution, while a neurotypical person may consider and weigh many options prior to choosing the best choice. This "one problem = one solution" thinking can be very helpful when more logical or cerebral tasks are required, but it can be a debilitating way of solving more emotional or relationship-based decisions that are anything but logical and cerebral. Our social engagements with others require quick and dynamic decision-making based on often rapidly changing criteria.

I had a mentor who shared her perspective about the autistic brain with me. When there is a problem to solve, she said, they typically only think of one solution rather than seeing a number of solutions and then selecting the best one. She stated that it was just how the autistic brain worked and there was no way to get around it. She suggested that we simply teach to that limited decision-making capability. Being the optimistic and strong-willed professional that I am, I decided to make it one of my missions to believe that people with autism are quite capable of dynamic decision-making if those around them support them appropriately. While the path of least resistance for the autistic mind may be that there is just one solution for each problem, I firmly stand by my professional opinion that they can consider and choose other options if those options are made clear. And one of the ways to bring clarity is through the use of the Sun Diagram.

Individuals with autism may feel chaotic or stuck in dynamic and ever-changing situations. As a result, they may have behaviors that do not work for them or those around them. For example, a person with autism may have extreme behaviors, such as throwing things, to indicate not wanting to do something. While their behavior is effective in stopping the interaction that may be stressing them, it is obviously not the best nor the only solution. Sharing and teaching alternatives that meet that same communication goal is key to the person succeeding and learning in different environments. Using visual representations of choices will help with that understanding.

The ability to consider a number of solutions to a given problem requires flexible thinking, consideration of alternatives, and imagining different outcomes. Without guidance, these are often quite challenging for individuals on the spectrum. The Sun Diagram is one way to help make choices clear and manageable by making them visual, narrowing choices, and engaging the individual in the process.

Ideally you would start drawing the Sun Diagram by putting the issue or problem in the center circle and then maybe two options out along two of the rays. For example, if a child is bored, you may put a bored face in the center of the sun, and one ray may be a word or drawing indicating listening to music while another ray may be reading a book. Only offer two or three of the options so that you can invite the autistic individual to add to it. The idea is that this would be a working diagram. You can explore what works and does not work for the person, adding or changing options that extend from each ray.

Remember that not all individuals with autism will recognize and understand words or line drawings. Again, we first learn that objects such as a cup or a bottle represent themselves when we see them before we understand line drawings and words. Bottom line: do not assume the person on the autism spectrum understands words when using the Sun Diagram. You may have to use actual objects, photos, or drawings in the center and for the rays. That said, I am consistently pleased with how much individuals with autism surprise me with their understanding of written words when I ensure joint attention and cocreate with them.

Use Visuals to Offer Structure

Many visual and organizational supports are based on extensive research of Structured Teaching by TEACCH Autism Program out of University of North Carolina, Chapel Hill. Structured Teaching has been around since the 1970s and is behind such evidence-based supports like work systems to increase independence and schedules for classrooms and daily routines.

The Structured Teaching approach capitalizes on the fact that many, if not most, autistic individuals thrive with routine and structure. They were the first to document the effectiveness of visuals described earlier in this chapter, such as the colored line drawings made into Velcro-backed laminated symbols representing a person's schedule. They stressed the importance of offering a person's schedule in a top-down or left-to-right orientation, for example, as research has shown that the autistic drive for completion will support them in completing the list-form schedule.

They also created what are called "work systems." These are extremely helpful, and gazillions of examples can easily be found on such sites as Pinterest. The basics are that you present a person with a task to do that is labeled "#1" followed by a task to do that is labeled "#2," and so on. When each task is completed, it goes into an "all finished" box or folder.

There are many ways you can get creative to help someone with auditory processing challenges connect, understand, and contribute to your interactions. Check out appendices 2 and 5 at the back of this book for more ideas to get your creativity flowing.

Use Video for More than Social Media

We are in an era when many of us now have video cameras in the palms of our hands in the form of our smartphones. We are able to access videos on how to fix a household appliance and post videos of our baby's first steps. Video now allows us to talk with one another across the country and across the world. We can upload photos and videos for others to enjoy on social media. Something you may not have thought of is using your video-capturing ability to help guide and better understand your interactions with that special person in your life with autism. Watching your own videos back can be extremely eye-opening as well as being informative for a person with autism.

You might video record an everyday task such as brushing teeth, for example. If you record from the moment your child walks into the bathroom, unscrews the cap on the toothpaste, squeezes toothpaste onto their toothbrush, and so on, you will be able to watch it back to observe your guiding behavior or your child's ability to complete the task. If the toothbrushing felt successful, you can use the video as a teaching tool for demonstrating success to your child, showing them the video when they may not feel as confident or remember the steps. They can watch, stop, rewind, and watch again as many times as they need to for understanding and confidence. You may choose to video someone else completing the task to then show the person to aid in their learning. This use of video as a teaching tool is called "video modeling," an evidence-based approach to guiding individuals with autism.

You also consider watching yourself on video as you are guiding. You can then review the video to determine how you might improve your connection and support—by using some of the concepts, tools, and strategies you learn in this book, for example. You might watch your video and realize on your own that you are talking too much and overshadowing your child's or partner's voice, for example. Or you may watch and realize that your partner would benefit from you slowing down. Additionally, you may watch it back and find that the interaction actually went much better and more smoothly than you thought in the moment.

Why We Touch

As a reminder, this chapter urges us to think of ways to communicate without relying on auditory processing. It's designed to stretch ourselves to consider all of the ways we communicate rather than just through the use of verbal words. As mentioned, people on the autism spectrum may not be able to process the spoken word as easily and may need the environment to give cues for their participation. We commonly use touch when we communicate with others, and it can be quite powerful. We use it to emphasize our concern for others by touching them gently on the arm and asking if they are all right. We may touch someone's hand to indicate our interest when dating or in friendship. We often crave touch with those we love yet bristle with unwanted or unexpected touch. That unwanted or unexpected touch often signals an invasion of our personal space.

Many adults on the spectrum share that they experience touch differently than others. They may experience some light touch as painful; the tiny water pellets from the shower on their skin may feel like needles, for example. But they feel other types of touch as deeply soothing, like the breeze when sitting outside in a quiet forest. Even parts of their bodies may be more sensitive than other parts, experiencing pain when touched on the face even gently while needing deep-pressure touch or squeezes on their arms for calming.

When I meet a teen or adult on the spectrum who shies away from touch with the people around them who love them, I am deeply saddened for them. I am saddened that they have learned that touch is something to be feared or simply not used in a loving relationship. Touch is such a human need and one that supports companionship and positive relationships.

In my workshops, I often have people turn to one another and tap each other on the shoulder as if they want or need something. You might consider putting down this book and finding someone who will do this with you. It is truly a felt experience. Have the other person tap your shoulder insistently and annoyingly. When someone touches you in this manner, they want you to stop what you are doing, shift to their agenda quickly, and do something at their request. Feels annoying, right? Now have your partner place a hand on your shoulder gently but firmly. That kind of touch feels very different. That feels more settling, soothing, and reassuring. It is not a message of "I need you to do this right now" but one of "I will wait until you are ready." The latter is so much more supportive of someone who needs time to shift their attention to you.

People on the autism spectrum may have experienced touch repeatedly and primarily when others need or want something from them. It is easy to fall into these patterns of interacting with people who do not shift their attention as readily and quickly. We try to rush them or cue them, at times incessantly. We end up touching them only when nagging or reminding.

Thankfully, this habitual use of touch and subsequent negative reaction can usually be remedied. Touch can again become one of connection and love through respect, observation, and mutual experimentation. But avoiding it is not the answer. Humans thrive when they have some level of physical connection in relationships and love.

You can and should deliberately and mindfully experiment with touch to support your relationship with someone with autism—whether it is your child, client, friend, or coworker. If you are not the person's close relative or have prior consent to touch them, be sure to gain consent first and do not touch with any element of surprise. And if they are able to tell you, ask them what types of touch are manageable for them.

Most adults on the spectrum report that unexpected touch is the most upsetting, and it may even be experienced as painful. Letting them know you are going to touch their arm by stating "I am going to touch your arm" as you slowly bring your hand to rest on their forearm will help them feel valued and respected.

Using Touch to Shift Attention

When you sit down beside an autistic person, their mind and attention may be on something else. They may be so deep in thought that they may not realize that you have come to sit next to them. Using the visual cue of your extended hand or the touch of your hand on their shoulder may significantly help them shift their attention to you so that you can engage socially.

Some individuals have the amazing ability to block out so much of their environment in favor of focusing on just one thing that when you touch them, they may not register your presence. That's when you need to offer firmer or even what I call "directional touch." What I mean by directional touch is that you may use your gentle but firm hand on their shoulder. Then move your hand slightly toward you as a gentle tug toward yourself as your bid for connection. You may have to experiment with what helps them shift their attention and also feels good for the individual with autism in your life.

I cannot state this enough: touch must be individualized for the person and not forced, but it should also not be avoided. Humans need touch that works for them to feel connected. In my work, I see that the well-intentioned people surrounding those with autism feel that they are respecting the person's sensory needs by simply not touching them or only touching them when the parent, partner, or caregiver wants or needs something. Neither of these lead to the acceptance, understanding, and social use of touch for gaining connection with others.

Start by simply experimenting with touch when you wish to share your kind and supportive thoughts with them. You might come near, slowly reach out and touch them on the shoulder, and say, "I'm glad you're here today," or "I love you." Try to include these moments while steering away from following the touch with a cue or demand. In fact, the touch does not have to be accompanied by any words. It is a way to connect with someone who may not be able to process auditory information as well as others can. Touch can stand alone as a way to let someone know that you value them.

Ensuring a balance between touching someone when you need or want something with touching someone when you wish to show you care is essential. Use touch to highlight your relationship and deepen your connection with the person in ways that work for both of you and that strengthen your love and connection.

CHAPTER 6

Allow Processing Time

I've listened enough. It's time for me to speak,
however it may sound. Through an electronic device,
my hands, or my mouth. Now it's your time to listen.
Are you ready?
—Neal Katz

I have worked hard to make this chapter truly demonstrate the enormity of this one practice for yourself and for the autistic individual with whom you are interacting. The trouble facing me is that it seems too simple at the surface. I am concerned you will gloss over this as a quick tip or strategy and not realize the critical nature of this for guiding independence and personal agency. Allowing processing time is simple: you need to give yourself and the other person time to think and respond authentically. It is in the application that the art comes into play, and the act of giving processing time makes the most difference for the autistic individual.

Why and how you give processing time matters. This one adjustment in your interactions can make a world of difference for people on the autism spectrum. It allows them to be present with you and to engage with you fully. It gives them the gift of our willingness to match their processing rather asking to always try and match ours. It gives them the opportunity to realize that their own unique contributions matter, giving rise to increased confidence and motivation.

Why Give Processing Time?

As you learned in the first chapter of this book regarding neuroscience research, we have discovered through infant eye gaze studies that babies who later develop autism take longer to disengage their attention from one stimulus before shifting it to another. The baby who later develops autism will take longer to disengage from looking at an original stimulus and shift their gaze to a competing stimulus. Fast-forward months and even years: that person continues to take more time than others to disengage and shift their attention. They also have had zillions of interactions where they were not in sync with what was being said, let alone with the nonverbal and more subtle cues we use for social engagement. As we reviewed in chapter 1, those interactions are crucial for a child's regulation and social development.

While the mechanisms for attending and shifting attention are there, it is just the act of disengaging and the timing of the shift that seem to create the challenges. Therefore, if you give the baby, child, teen, or adult time to disengage from one stimulus and shift their attention, you will be modifying your interactions so they can be at their best. If you continue to talk, engage, direct, or cue the person before they are ready, you are simply adding to their internal stress of trying to keep up or adding to their flood. They may respond with coping mechanisms, including talking over you, monologuing, or saying no simply to gain processing time.

I also mentioned in chapter 1 of this book that additional research indicates that being in sync with someone else promotes what is called "prosocial behavior." Prosocial behavior describes the actions that we choose to take to benefit someone else. When you open a door for someone who is running in from the rain, hold the elevator, or pick up someone's dropped keys, you are behaving in a prosocial manner. Many of the children, teens, and adults I see are very inwardly focused, not realizing their impact on others. They also do not realize that prosocial behaviors can significantly improve relationships. A child crying on the playground may be comforted by another child reaching out to them. The teen who draws a picture of an anime character for a new friend who likes anime makes that person feel valued. The bottom line is that people with autism may need practice being in sync with others to then feel the drive to be prosocial and consider their impact on those around them.

Being in sync with someone requires that initial attention shift or the whole interaction is off-kilter. Let's consider the back-and-forth tennis match analogy again. If the server is lobbing the ball over the net so fast that the receiving person cannot hit it back, the server has a choice to either continue to serve at that intensity and speed or make adjustments to encourage a nice volley with the receiving player. The manner in which you offer a bid for engagement with the person with autism can either be fast and lobbed well across the room without the chance of being received, *or* you can first wait for the receiving player to indicate their readiness before lobbing the ball so that it can be successfully hit back to you. Similarly, if we serve a ball over the net without waiting for the person to be ready and we simply repeat the serve, speed up, or change too quickly, we potentially ruin the start of what could have been a nice game of tennis.

One of my client-parents recently made the realization that she was not giving her son enough time to be ready for that bid for engagement. She would repeat her cues out of love and attempt to clarify her cue. She might say something like, "Do you want to color?" then rapidly move on to simplifying her wording to "Want to color?" before asking next "Do you want green or orange?" Each of these kind invitations was in the hopes that one would stick or land. She wanted one of the bids to make sense enough for her son to then respond.

What she realized was that with each additional bid for connection with her, he was still working to process the first bid. When the next bid came in, he was either flustered or his processing clock had to restart from zero again. With each bid, he would try to respond, but then a new bid would override the first. He would get flooded and either shut down or become aggressive. She has now learned to offer a single bid and wait patiently.

Assume the person with whom you wish to engage is experiencing an environment that is overwhelming, chaotic, or at the very least, distracting. They have not had practice with attention shifting in the same way that you likely have. Imagine how hard they have to work at learning and engaging with the world. They have had to glean information as it flies by, unable to truly engage with the information in the same way as a neurotypical person. Any new stimulus is thrown at them while they are still working to engage and disengage from the last stimulus. And in our world, there are so many things to look at, listen to, engage with, and learn.

Learn to Identify Defensive Habits

People can get very creative in ensuring what they need to survive in our busy world. If someone needs processing time, they may have myriad ways of responding that provide them that time to shift their attention, think, and respond. The most common way to gain this time is by saying no or walking away. Based on numerous previous experiences of not being given the time to process, they may not even try. Stating no to invitations keeps them safe.

The tricky part to consider here is that autistics may have developed ways to gain processing time that may not be obvious. Some may say no to anything being offered before they hear the specifics about the offer, while others may repeat the last word you said rather than having a true yes or no response. Still others may have become completely cue-dependent, not having had the opportunity to practice their personal authentic responses due to always playing catch-up.

I've seen clients exhibit challenging behaviors, including loud and annoying vocalizations to drown out the noise around them, just to gain time to think. I've met others who shut down and become silent or retreat to their bedrooms in lieu of engaging in interactions where they are not afforded processing time. Imagine if all they need is more time to shift their attention, think for themselves, and offer their own contributions to the world.

If you are now committing to give more processing time to someone you support or are wishing to befriend, do not expect immediate results. They may need some time to settle in to the new you and the new space for processing that you are giving them. They may need to build trust that you really do understand their processing and respect their authentic voice.

Steps for Giving Someone Processing Time

Now that you have learned the essentials for why we offer processing time, I suspect you'd also like to know how and when to offer it. In this next section, I offer you simple steps that you can take as you learn and experiment together.

CHECK IN WITH YOURSELF FIRST

Giving someone processing time sounds simple—and it can be simple. First you must have your own body and mind calm and ready to fully listen. You must first find your own openness and readiness to attend not just to their words, but also to the other ways they may communicate their processing. Consider doing these things for yourself first:

- Sit down if you can.
- Breathe deeply.
- Soften your body language and facial expressions.
- If you need to go back and read chapter 3 on self-calming and self-soothing, please do. These must and always come first.

CHECK YOUR EXPECTATIONS

Next, consider your expectations of the other person. If you have low expectations of their ability to engage with you, even with processing time provided, you will potentially and tragically offer baby talk, or you will speak down to the person. This is not our goal. Our goal is to speak to the person at their age level. Simplify your wording, presume competence, and give them time to shift their attention.

OFFER A BID TO CONNECT

A bid to connect in this context is any opening to a social exchange. Bids can be verbal or nonverbal, but they are always meant to evoke a contingent response from another person. Here are some examples of bids to connect:

- When greeting, extending your hand to someone to shake
- Extending your hand to help someone stand up
- Saying or waving hello
- Starting to reach for something while gazing to the person who is closer to what you are reaching for

- Extending a toy, a piece of food, or paper
- Opening your arms while orienting to another person, positioned for a hug
- Pointing to something and gazing to your partner to show or label it
- Starting a sentence and allowing your partner to finish it

When offering the bid, do not expect a specific response. Allow your partner to respond in their own unique or personalized manner. A directive like "Give that to me" is not a bid for a contingent and unique response. It may be contingent, but it does not invoke any personalized response nor one that will potentially expand your interaction.

WAIT EXPECTANTLY

This is the gold. This is giving processing time. Once you have offered the bid, wait. Stay in the position of offering the bid. Do not sit down if you're standing, give up if you have offered a toy, or turn away if you have asked a question. Stay poised and ready to receive the other person's contingent response. Expect it, presume competence, and wait patiently. If you have extended your hand, leave your hand extended while you wait. If you have pointed at something and are gazing to your partner, stay positioned for their verbal or nonverbal response to your action.

COUNT SILENTLY

Keep your facial expressions and body positioning expectant and ready to receive their ideas, their thoughts, their emotions.

Watch their body language and facial expressions. If they remain in the immediate vicinity—even if they are engaging in seemingly off-task behaviors like spinning, flapping, gazing away, staring at you, or looking down—assume they are processing. Count in your head up to sixty—yes, sixty. It may seem like a lot, but we never give each other enough time to process, and people with autism and auditory processing challenges will need more than most people.

LATHER, RINSE, REPEAT

As you continue to engage in a back-and-forth with someone with autism, it may be a bit slower of a feedback loop, especially at first, but attempt to find a rhythm. You offer a bid, you give them processing time, they respond. You offer another bid, you give them processing time, they respond, and so on.

You will notice that processing time will be quick for some things and take much longer for others. The more open-ended your bid, the more time it may take for the person to decide which action to take. Maybe you extend your hand and get a quick handshake or response of some sort. When you ask, "How are you?" it may take much longer for someone to sort through their thoughts to determine an answer that is most appropriate for that exchange.

A long time ago, I worked with an eight-year-old boy and his parents who were struggling to get him to do things. The son's affect was flat, and they were concerned about depression. Both parents were high energy and competitive athletes. They had other children who joined them in their competitive board gaming and sport activities and so were perplexed when their son with autism would not join them.

I observed that his parents would cue him through almost all of his responses, trying to get him to speed up. His only job was to comply with their cues: "Do this," "Do that," "Come here," "Put this here." He was not given any personal agency to offer his own unique ideas or learn from what he was doing. He was simply in react mode. I guided his parents to slow down, allow processing time, and count up to sixty in their heads. They struggled to do so, as it conflicted with their competitive natures, but they were willing to try.

Almost immediately, they saw that their son was fully willing and capable of independently responding when provided with more processing time. Their exchanges and their partnerships went from being very one-sided to being more enjoyable, complex, and relationship building—just by giving him more time to process his own unique contributions within their interactions.

Over time and with practice, his mood lifted, and his processing time sped up. He moved out of being so cue-dependent and on to developing his own unique and wonderful personality.

An amazing byproduct of allowing or affording someone processing time is that you also bolster their personal agency.

The person who has not been given time to truly participate can now make the realization that they have control over their own actions in relation to others and what happens around them. Instead of being cued through life, either expecting or relying on others to tell them what to do, they can now share their unique ideas. The person who shuts downs, retreats, or ignores requests may now realize they can contribute without feeling rushed and anxious. The person who seems to challenge every directive can now relax into not having to fight to gain processing time.

CHAPTER 7

Decluttering the Environment

Behavior is communication.
Change the environment and behaviors will change.
—Lana David

Autistic adults will commonly share that the sensory information around them is coming in all at the same level, without a filter. The sound of the car horn comes in at the same level as the buzz and brightness from the fluorescent lights and the sound of voices. The labels on every item in the grocery store may demand immediate and full attention as the autistic adult attempts to walk down an aisle looking for the milk at the back of the store. The lights, signs, and people's clothing all command attention at the same time and at the same priority level.

I can only imagine if the car horn outside the window, the dog barking next door, or the truck passing by on the street all sounded as if they were right next to me. I would be in a constant state of hypervigilance. To keep myself safe, I would need to listen for and monitor all sounds, or I may think I could be run over, bitten, or attacked. Since our neurological systems were not made for constant hypervigilance, I would need to be in predictably quiet environments to feel safe to calm my system.

One of my long-time clients who is nonverbal will visibly become agitated and fearful at times. When we are together, I have also noticed that his hearing is significantly better than mine. I may not hear the person walking and talking softly outside my office until I notice that he has been distracted by them. But when I label the sound—"That is someone just walking by and talking on the phone"—he will calm quickly and return to task.

Recently there was loud construction going on nearby on my street. We could hear the construction trucks and machinery off in the distance. He was obviously distracted but intrigued by the noises. He did not seem fearful, as he was not grimacing or making soft, fearful noises. He was sitting up, attentive to the sounds. I asked him, "Do you want to go see what is making that noise?" He signed his "Yes!" and stood up. We walked around the block and identified what was making the noise. He gazed at the construction work then quickly and independently returned to my office and to the work we were doing as if his curiosity had been satisfied.

Another time we heard someone upstairs making a lot of noise. I knew they were painting the space above my office. Again I asked him if he wanted to go see what was making the noise. He signed quickly and definitively "Yes," and we went up to see. He took a moment to see what it was and then returned to our work. What this taught me was that once he knew what it was making the noise and could connect the noise with the visual, he could feel calm, relaxed, and safe.

Turn Down the Noise

When we talk about decluttering, we often think of visual clutter. Yet it is essential to also declutter the auditory environment for and with a person with autism. Here are some ways we can do that:

- Turn off the television, radio, or video playing in the background.
- Choose to meet in a space that is away from the hustle and bustle.
- Avoid talking to others over that person—especially during transitions that are already chaotic.
- Reduce talking to a minimum whenever possible.

In addition to simply reducing the overall "background" clutter, we can also declutter our own words. Say only as much as needed and only when the person's attention is shifted to you. Simplify your wording to only the essentials. So instead of saying, "I think you might like to join me to go for a walk. It is such a nice day," you might say, "Let's go for a walk." This will support the person in hearing the essence of your communication rather than making them wade through all of the other words.

Respect the overall amount of verbal communication between you. If they are silent, choose to be silent as well. Use gestures or facial expressions to engage, or sit beside them in comfortable silence. If the person is using one- or two-word phrases, you might also. Keeping balanced verbal communication can support the back-and-forth reciprocity between you without creating an overwhelmed state.

Slow down and allow the person's attention to shift to you before talking. This should reduce the overall amount of speech you use, as it may take a bit longer for them to communicate their thoughts. Allow the person's curiosity and attention to shift to you before talking. Curiosity to You, or C2U, is a critical and essential element to guiding someone on the autism spectrum. It allows your guidance to be optimally felt, heard, and integrated by the individual.

Pay Attention to Visual Details

I think of visual decluttering as especially important for those people who are less verbal. It seems that they rely more heavily on the visual information around them, as they commonly struggle more significantly with auditory processing. In order to make sense of their world, they have to attend keenly to the visual information presented then wade through uncertainty and determine what is expected of them, as illustrated in the following examples:

- A ten-year-old boy I knew would walk into his classroom every day and be the first to notice whether the date on the calendar in the room had been updated. If it had not, he would take it upon himself to change it for the class.
- A nineteen-year-old young adult would walk into my office and notice immediately if one or more of my shelved books was out of alphabetical order.
- A seven-year-old boy drew accurate and extensive maps of neighborhoods he had been to only once, complete with house addresses and street signs.

These examples all demonstrate the acuity and attention to visual information presented. Now, if you were primarily using that information to navigate the world, you may appreciate having less to wade through to get to the important information. The ten-year-old who walked into his classroom and noticed the calendar immediately may find it helpful to have fewer things on the walls around said calendar. If there were pictures, wires, cords, and additional words surrounding that calendar (as there very often are), he may have to concentrate harder and be less available for the interaction and engagement with those around him, including with his peers.

I know for myself that when I am overwhelmed emotionally, my work and home space may also mirror that inner chaos, becoming equally cluttered. My clothes may not get put away as quickly. The books and mail may get scattered onto the countertop rather than sorted and put away. And when I choose to take a few moments to clear that visual clutter, my mind will often follow and feel less overwhelmed, more organized, and more settled. One of my clients would dump everything in her room onto the floor. It was frustrating for her family. It seemed that when she felt disorganized, overwhelmed, or unsettled, she would dump her collections of toys and items as if to match how she felt internally. As she felt better, she would "clean" her space by shoving items into buckets, drawers, and closets to have them out of sight.

Many people on the autism spectrum appreciate visual organization. We can tap into a person's natural drive for order in our support towards independence. We may create a work system or task, for example, with a very clear order in which it must be done. This may include file folders that indicate "first, do this worksheet," then "second, do this one," and "third, do this one."

By organizing a person's space and tasks with a clear visual order, we can back off our direct cues and what feels like micromanaging. This allows the person to feel their own independence and personal agency. For additional ideas for decluttering and organizing the visual environment for someone with autism, please consider an internet search for TEACCH's Structured Teaching ideas. There are plenty.

Consider Your Own Odor

It follows that if someone's senses are heightened, they may also have a heightened olfactory sense, or sense of smell. I learned early in my work with people with autism to not wear perfume or strongly scented hair products. They can be distracting and send someone into overload. It is best to simply go with scentless products whenever possible.

Not everyone with autism will be hypersensitive. There are plenty who are hyposensitive, meaning they are under-responsive to sensory input and may not be bothered at all by your perfumes and aftershave.

Declutter the Emotional Landscape

Here is another shoutout for taking care of yourself. People with autism can often feel your emotions, your anxiety, and your trepidation more than you may realize. Some may experience emotions as colors, hues, or even as sound. By keeping your own emotional landscape in check, you can ensure a solid base for your autistic partner and you to engage most successfully.

The more we can consider and declutter the overall visual, auditory, olfactory, and emotional environment for ourselves and for our partners (autistic or not), the more we are creating a respectful and safe space for engaging with one another.

CHAPTER 8

Respecting Sensory Needs and Processing

My autism makes things shine. Sometimes I think it is amazing, but sometimes it is sad when I want to be the same and talk the same and I fail. Playing the piano makes me very happy. Playing Beethoven is like your feelings—all of them—exploding.
—Mikey Allcock

When we feel physically threatened, the areas of our brains that help us move and react quickly are activated, while the brain integration that is required for deeper contemplation is thwarted. Our amygdala takes over or "hijacks" our brains, causing what is known as the "fight, flight, freeze, or faint" response. This ability for our brains to adjust to sensory input keeps us safe in the face of danger.

Many autistic individuals I have met are in this state of hypervigilance much of the time. Their sensory systems are screaming that they are in danger even when others around them may not experience the environment or situation in the same way. Autistics may react to this sensory or emotional onslaught by acting out or striking others in their vicinity to get away from the stimulus that their bodies perceive as danger. Others may react to the perceived danger by retreating and going inward, hyper-focusing on toys, activities, or routines. And still others may have sensory systems that are considered hyposensitive, or much less sensitive than average, with some sensory information while being hyper-sensitive to others.

I met one of my favorite autistic celebrities, Dr. Stephen Shore, at an Autism Society of America conference many years ago. I was so excited to meet him and take a picture with him that I am sure I embarrassed myself terribly. But I digress. Dr. Shore uses an activity with his audiences that I have adopted for my presentations as well. A small group of people gather around one person who's in the middle. Each person surrounding the one in the middle does something to engage and interact with the person in different, sometimes annoying, ways. The person in the middle experiences sensory overload combined with performance anxiety, as they are also tasked with trying to respond to comprehension questions in a text being read to them. Most people have visceral responses to this activity and share that they want to scream, hit, shut down, or run out of the room.

Sound familiar? These are commonly autistic behaviors we try to remedy through behavioral modifications rather than addressing from a neurological, biological, and normal response to threat. I am hoping you are seeing the theme that we must respect sensory processing rather than just "fix" behaviors.

Observe Your Partner

The first step to support and honor someone who experiences sensory and emotional information differently is to observe or ask them directly. The person may show you how they are processing information with their body language and where they shift their attention. They may tilt their head slightly when a truck goes by in the distance or an airplane is heard very far away. They may flick their fingers in front of their eyes or simply seem entranced by the dust failing through the beam of sunlight coming through the window. They may pace when thinking, fidget with their fingers while talking, or even twist their bodies into various shapes when starting to feel stress or anxiety.

By slowing down and respecting that they may need to move or engage with the world around them in a different way, we can begin to connect more deeply. By allowing someone to shift their attention from the sensory or emotional experience before we add to it, we provide a respectful space for interaction.

It may take some time, but write down what you observe in yourself or your partner regarding how they may sense the world around them. These will be clues for you of things to either avoid, reduce, or integrate into your interactions together.

Sensory Integration versus Sensory Satiation

Some people do their best thinking when they are doing something else at the same time. This is called sensory integration when extra sensory input is integrated into other activities. Some need to be moving, for example, while interacting with others or chewing gum to focus on an activity. Still others may need to listen to music or even static white noise while trying to listen to a classroom teacher, coach, or friend.

Other people do their best thinking and processing if they have first had their sensory needs satiated prior to trying to focus and attend to an activity. They may need to jump on a trampoline or run a mile in the morning before they start their day. They may need regular breaks to jump, pace, or chew something. Offering regular sensory satiation is frequently called a "sensory diet," as someone may need to ration the sensory activity throughout the day, just as you might with food, with small snacks or meals throughout the day.

I often recommend using a "bite box" full of things someone can chew on or bite. Offer these items three to four times per day to individuals who struggle with mouthing or even biting at inappropriate times. It can fulfill or satiate the need for that input temporarily so that they can focus on new learning and engagement. If you or someone you know seems to be seeking sensory input so much that it's getting in the way, consider putting a few choices into a box that you offer routinely through the day.

Different Types of Sensory Input and Support

While each person is very different from another, there are three types of sensory input that can commonly support those on the autism spectrum. You can offer these either integrated within activities or at routine intervals to satiate. You will have to experiment with what works best for yourself or the autistic person you know. Please refer to an occupational therapist for more individualization and specification. I have also included a more detailed list that I use with clients in the appendix.

The three types of sensory input are:

- Deep-pressure: Massage is one example of this kind of touch.
- Proprioceptive: This commonly uses resistance to joints, tendons, and muscles found in gross motor activities.
- Vestibular: This usually consists of movement activities, like the movement of the head in space.

In general, slow, deep, or heavy input tends to calm. Fast, intense, or irregular stimulation tends to alert. Autistic individuals have very strong and very different sensory experiences. These sensory supports must be individualized based on the person's differences, preferences, and sensitivities. It may surprise you to find that what is alerting to you may be calming for them, or vice versa. Experimenting with what works best for yourself as well as your child or partner will be key to discovering proper sensory supports. Accessing and consulting with an occupational therapist who specializes in sensory support and regulation is also key.

Performance Anxiety

Most people on the autism spectrum tend to become overwhelmed with sensory stimulation, especially if they are asked to perform while in the sensory-full environment. By "performing," I mean asking questions of them or asking them to transition to something else. I do not mean getting on stage in front of everyone, which is commonly what causes performance anxiety in the general population. Interestingly, people with autism can often tolerate and even enjoy fully immersive sensory experiences like concerts or busy swim centers. In those situations, they are not being asked to do anything; they are being entertained. However, the minute you try to engage within that setting, the same person may become overwhelmed. The addition of social demands can elicit performance anxiety. I think of it as an added emotional experience that makes those floodgates break.

Sensory input is often experienced in very different ways for each person on the spectrum. Sights and sounds may be fascinating to one person but annoying or unbearable for another. A fire alarm or a person singing may cause utter panic for one person, while another may not even seem to notice. One person may be considered hypersensitive to sights and/or sounds, making it difficult for them to manage in the community without headphones, dark glasses, or a baseball cap to shield their eyes. Others may be hyposensitive, driving them to be "sensory seekers," seeking out strong smells, strong tastes, loud music, or intense bodily input, like running into people or walls, or jumping hard on a trampoline.

The key is to consider that someone on the autism spectrum is more likely to experience their environment around them in very different ways than someone who is neurotypical. And as Dr. Stephen Shore reminds us, "If you have met one person with autism, you have only met one person with autism." While there are similarities, everyone with autism is different.

Part II

Are You Seeing Autism?

By applying the information you glean in this book, you are one step closer to seeing autism. And by seeing autism, you will be better equipped to connect with someone on the spectrum. Seeing them may be the only intervention that is necessary.

What stood out to you in this section?
What would you like to remember?

Not Relying on
Auditory Processing

Allowing Processing Time

Decluttering the Environment

Respecting Sensory
Needs and Processing

Part II

Are You
Seeing Clearly?

PART III

PRACTICE

*It is only through practice that we learn
that failure is a vehicle for learning.*

CHAPTER 9

Getting Curious

Autism...offers a chance for us to glimpse an awe-filled
vision of the world that might otherwise pass us by.
—Dr. Colin Zimbleman

Without curiosity, interactions with others are limited, one-way, and not very satisfying. Without curiosity, interactions become task oriented or only exist to get someone to do something. With curiosity, your interactions come to life via new learning and experiences.

Everyone has experienced less-than-fulfilling interactions where someone just talks at you versus with you. This might have been a store clerk or someone you were meeting for the first time at a gathering of friends. It is the opposite that supports our feelings of kinship with others. When someone is curious about you and you are curious about them, you gain that back-and-forth feedback system that has a synchrony and that feels good and energizing. You feel validated, heard, and seen.

Never a day goes by that I do not feel blessed by the fact that my daily work with individuals and families experiencing autism engages with my own curiosity about each person's strengths and interests. I listen. I ask questions. I am fascinated. I love learning from every person with autism I meet and their family members. Each person has so much to teach me and the worldwide community. I hope to bestow that enjoyment and deep curiosity in you as well. It is a joy to get to know someone who thinks differently than you do. You get a whole new perspective on the world. In the last section of this book, "Holding on to Hope," I share stories about members in our worldwide community who are making change both on a large scale and in our everyday lives.

To review and center ourselves again on the research shared in chapter 1, we are learning that autistics have challenges with disengaging from one stimulus, topic, or activity and shifting their attention to something or someone else. A person's autistic behaviors, which may be challenging to you, are not intentional or manipulative. They are responses to a developmental cascade effect. If there are time delays with social reciprocity early in life, a child's experience with interactions would be awkward and the timing would be off.

With cognition intact, the child would still learn to get their needs met. You may have a child or partner who speaks at you rather than with you, for example. You may have an autistic who makes requests with beautiful eye contact but avoids that eye contact at almost all other times. Here, you are learning that by adjusting your speed and allowing more time to shift, you can bring that social reciprocity to life. Making the time and space for the person with autism to shift their attention and initiate with you can be golden. They will feel valued and respected. It will also allow them to demonstrate their true nature, which is commonly to be curious, kind, and extremely knowledgeable.

Of course, this may not work immediately for connection, as many autistics have had so many years of being out of sync with others that this may feel unsettling at first. There is an old adage that we have two ears and only one mouth so we can listen more than we talk. People with autism tend to get talked over, pushed aside, and overwhelmed more often than they are truly listened to. Making the choice to listen more, get curious, and talk less around autistic individuals will give way to significantly more satisfying synchrony between you. You may experience an awkward timing at first, but you will see that when you engage in this way, the back-and-forth becomes smooth and rewarding over time.

Engage with Special Interests

When you choose to be curious about someone else, you give them the gift of your time, energy, and engagement. And when the person with autism feels seen and heard, they gain confidence by feeling included and celebrated. Often autistic people have special interests that are not necessarily in line with yours or with others' around them. Some people with autism may enjoy the concreteness and visual organization of Lego while others may like anime, playing video games, or organizing their clothes or stuffed animals. Still other people may love to tell you every fact they know about trains, routes, or departure schedules—they enjoy the complexity and the certainty of the information. Some may not be able to verbally tell you about something, but they can draw detailed cityscapes or objects from memory. And some others can be so enthralled with nature that they pick up individual leaves along their walk just to see them fall and glisten in the light.

I enjoy getting to know my clients, especially the teens and adults, through playing games. I usually start with a basic card game, giving them a choice as to which card game they'd like to play. I can assess quickly whether they are intrigued or bored with my offer and will make adjustments accordingly. If the person is intrigued but unable to follow intricate rules of a game, I might switch tactics and make it into a "put in" game, where we take turns putting the cards into a container. Similarly I might move to a matching by color or by number game. I follow the child's interest by getting curious about their engagement in the moment. It is through this curiosity about my clients that I have been introduced to the amazing games of Magic: The Gathering, Dungeons & Dragons, and strategy-based board games.

While meeting and getting to know my clients, I get curious about what they are curious about rather than trying to steer them immediately to my agenda. Again, if the core issue of autism is social reciprocity, we can relax and create moments of that social reciprocity in anything just by being curious! We can integrate social reciprocity practice into any activity, so why not the ones they find enjoyable, safe, and intriguing?

If we cannot be curious about someone's special interests, we are closing off a significant avenue of connection with that person. The more that we can find a way to be curious about how or why they are thinking about a given topic, the more they can share with us their processing, their wisdom, and their curiosity. We can learn through these special interests about what works and does not work for them.

For example, if a young child seems interested in letters and numbers, they are indicating that they like sameness, routine, and are probably going to be an early reader. They also probably have an incredible attention to detail, especially visual infor-mation. If someone is especially intrigued with war history and gaming, they may be deeply curious about how people in history figured out complicated political or emotional interactions. If they are more interested in the facts or figures, they might find those comforting, especially when life becomes more complex, as in most social interactions.

Be in the Moment

People who are nonverbal are often tuned in to things that you and I may not have experienced before. If we get curious in the moment, we may have our eyes opened to something we hadn't slowed down enough to notice.

We, as neurotypicals, strive daily and set personal life goals to "be in the moment," to "meditate regularly," to "stop and smell the roses." People with autism are not often worried about the past or the future; they are in the here and now. They observe the space, the sounds, and the feelings of things around them, where others ignore and miss details that they take in. When sharing a story or information that is import-ant to them, they frequently take their time and do not worry about the extraneous societal demands around them. While this can be frustrating when you are in a hurry, it can also be refreshing if you are not. Most people with autism need time to shift their attention and to engage fully, so when they do, it is rich and powerful.

Some people with autism know more about facts and figures on certain topics than most people. This can be fascinating if you let it be. One person may know a lot about steam engines, having studied them almost exclusively for most of their lives. Others may know more than the average person about World War II or be able to name seemingly endless pieces of classical music, including the composers and musicians, within just a few notes of hearing the tune.

Most people with autism are incredibly literal. This too can also be refreshing if you let it be. It takes the silly social complexity out of situations. It makes stating what you wish to say to them easier: the blunter you are, the better that person will hear you and the more comfortable they'll feel. The more you dance around your words, adding worry, anxiety, and concern, the more you stress the person by adding too much complexity that might not matter anyway. Instead of worrying about what they mean or what they said or didn't say, you can usually rest assured that if something mattered enough, they would say it plainly. Concrete and literal interpretations abound.

Many autistics are quite comfortable on the computer and are able to navigate the gaming world with a nimbleness that seems incongruent with their other activities in daily life. Similarly, some can engage in and excel in such games as Dungeons & Dragons—full of imagery, strategy, and interaction—but not seem motivated to work or go to school. We make a grave mistake when we assume that someone with autism is lazy or unmotivated. While their outward appearance may seem that way, their inaction is often rooted in a deep-seated fear of failure. And the more that we point out the person's weaknesses, rather than celebrate their strengths, the more we perpetuate their inaction. By digging deep, listening fully, being curious, and celebrating strengths, we build confidence, which enables action and promotes engagement.

Everyone needs to be celebrated. Everyone needs to have times and places where we feel strong and confident. Be sure that the person with autism has times and places for sharing their strengths and interests. If they have an interest that seems more of an obsession, do not eliminate it completely. You will only make it stronger or seriously negate the person's individuality. Instead, set clear limits as to a time or place when it is appropriate. Being told you can never talk about something ever again can be soul-crushing. It is very different to be told that someone would love to hear about your special interest from six to six thirty each night.

Don't Be Afraid to Offer Challenges

Get curious about your child or partner's reactions to challenges. Challenges are opportunities for individuals to think and make decisions for themselves. Challenges can be open-ended questions, like "How was your day?" or they can be as simple as offering them a jar that is hard to open. Opening the jar will usually help the person feel needed and useful in addition to providing a challenge. Everyone likes to be helpful when elicited in a kind manner.

Track your invitations to help figure out what works and what doesn't work for supporting the individual to boost their confidence. Start small. Do not demand, but provide the opportunity for them to be helpful based on your nonverbal gestures or your statements of need. Here are some examples of challenges you might offer depending on the age of your child or partner:

- Struggle to open a bag of something, then hold it out for them to give it a try rather than saying, "Open this." Simply show nonverbally that you need their assistance.
- Have your hands full as you approach a door, pause, and gaze to them. If there's no response, state, "I'd love your help," but please stay away from "Open the door for me." You will read more about why in the next chapter on using mindful communication.
- Sit down together at the dinner table and be missing something, such as forks, water, or plates. Look to them curiously to see if they might be able to help.
- When they come to ask you to do something, offer to help, but do not do the whole thing for them. Offer ideas to consider but not solutions. Please refer to the 50% Rule described in chapter 11.

With each offer, observe and take note of your partner's reaction. Do they jump at the opportunity to be helpful? Do they bristle when you even approach them wanting their help? Or do they start to help but then give up, unable to sustain their attention to the task? Each of these answers will help you understand where the person may need practice and guidance in small doses to build their confidence.

Additionally, I hope that you will take a few minutes to use the reflections in the back of this section. Assess and get curious about your ability to be in the moment, to authentically explore the way your partner thinks and processes. If you are unable to do this, please take the time to determine why that may be the case. For example, if your partner aggravates you every time they tell you another train fact, ask yourself if you are taking enough time for yourself. When you do, you may be better able to see through their repetition to see their true intention of engaging with you.

CHAPTER 10

Using Mindful Communication

Autists are the ultimate square pegs, and the problem with pounding a square peg into a round hole is not that the hammering is hard work. It's that you're destroying the peg.
—Paul Collins

Communication between humans is amazingly complex. It's surprising that it is successful at all. Communication includes body language, facial expressions, tone of voice, sound effects, and even the distance you are from your partner and the clothes you wear. Even more depends on the culture in which you live and the experiences you have had to get you to that point in time. It is important to remember that the verbal aspect of communication is just one small element of communication.

In autistic development, the child seems more drawn to the predictable aspects of their environments rather than the more dynamic and changing elements, like the social nuances of communication. Objects, toys, and labels for things become central, while the more social aspects and dynamics fade to the background. The child who later develops autism may seem more motivated by inanimate objects or memorizing details. The concrete thinking gets established early and is reinforced by environmental opportunities and interactions. As the child stops seeking the dynamic aspects of communication, the child's caregivers logically shift their way of communicating with the child to be more concrete and primarily verbal. The communication between them becomes more predictable, directive, and cue driven. The child grows and develops within a loving and caring system that compensates and adapts to the child's strengths. But this is not a healthy long-term solution.

One of the beauties of our humanity is that we shift and adapt to changes. We have seen that our own thinking changed with the COVID-19 pandemic, for example. We are not only capable of making adaptations to our thinking, but we shift to new ways of being that become natural. During the pandemic, for example, wearing masks around others no longer looked as awkward or unusual as it had before.

It is easy to fall into trying to teach someone everything they need to know through prompting and directing them. In our Western society, however, when children turn eighteen, they need to be able to think for themselves. The world is not a place where we will thrive if we are dependent on prompts from others. If we need to be cued to put our shoes on, get dressed, make food, say hello, bathe, brush our teeth, and more, we remain locked in a world of compliance rather than choice, personal understanding, and independence. Being in a world of compliance makes a person either comply or resist. When one is cue-dependent, there is no negotiation, no personal freedom, no growth, no challenge to be more. The world becomes either "to do or not to do" rather than a world of experimenting with what works and does not work for one's own personality and values.

Sadly I see a lot of clients enter my services as teens and adults who have deeply grooved habits of either being completely compliant with no initiation muscles *or* they are completely resistant and shut down—also with no initiation muscles. Many want to be independent but are not equipped to carry that load. These teens and adults are at a loss to make the decisions for themselves in everyday life that set the stage for other life decisions, like careers or relationships.

Now the good news: you can alter the way that you, as a parent, friend, or professional, communicate with an autistic person of any age to help them strengthen those muscles of personal decision-making that will break them out of the compliance or noncompliance loop. I have found that people with autism do not need to be taught the skills but do need to be supported to use them in various contexts—again, to build the muscle. And just like strength training, it takes practice and determination from both the coach and the athlete. It is not just a scenario we can set up and expect the person to simply comply. We must meet the person where they are and get to know how deep they are in the well-worn groove of compliance in order to build trust and connection. We can offer tiny opportunities to engage their thinking, processing, and helpfulness. We give these as confidence-building opportunities to honor and respect their own ability to make decisions through the way we interact and communicate.

The person on the spectrum can alter their own trajectory of development and engagement at any age. As you may remember, "what fires together, wires together" in our brains. When a guide alters their communication style in critical ways, it can shift a person's attention from the static or concrete elements of communication to more of the full, dynamic communication. And full and dynamic communication supports relationship building and personal decision-making. When someone is more in tune with nonverbal communication between people, they will be better attuned to the emotional well-being of others. When someone is engaged in communication that is less directive and cued by others, they learn to make decisions for themselves rather than relying on those around them.

As well-meaning parents, professionals, and partners, we tend to jump in to fix situations for our children and partners. We want life to be less stressful, so we avoid challenges. As I mentioned in chapter 4, this can set a person up for learned helplessness, which is associated with low self-esteem and lack of motivation. We need to deliberately engage and involve individuals with autism in everyday decision-making. We need to deliberately elicit their help with problems. With this daily engagement, we give the person the necessary practice in solving problems for themselves or others. Being able to solve increasingly complex problems is required for long-term quality of life and well-being.

We as humans are put into a multitude of situations requiring decision-making in often rapidly changing circumstances. Expecting an individual to go from childhood, where decisions are made for them, to adulthood and making decisions for themselves can be too big of a leap for many. Being scheduled in school as to where you go, who you see, and what you need to do is very different than initiating a job search or navigating a busy college dorm life. By mindfully giving practice with decision-making in smaller everyday moments, we can help someone build that muscle so that they can confidently address bigger or more nuanced problems later.

Talk Less so Your Partner Has a Chance to Think

By decreasing how much you talk, you allow more processing time for your partner. By decreasing the sheer number of words you say, you also provide practice with the fullness of body language, facial expressions, and gestures. You give your child or partner a chance to talk or communicate with you, because you are not taking up all of the space. If you are doing all of the talking, you are also doing all of the thinking. We need to provide opportunities for our children and partners to have confident voices and engage in decision-making opportunities— not overcompensate and think for them.

Young children (under five years of age) are still learning how to communicate. There are professionals who may recommend the intense use of verbal modeling with a child who is nonverbal. If the child is on the spectrum, we must be aware of and sensitive to the potential overwhelm from sensory input and the child's focus on the concrete elements of speech. Without this knowledge, you may simply bombard their system with additional information to process rather than making what you say come to life and make sense.

Many children on the spectrum will, for example, learn words and labels for specific items or locations. It is not unusual for children with autism spectrum differences to label favorite foods or restaurants before being able to greet someone, for example. Or they may learn a whole phrase to mean just one thing, as seen in echolalia. Someone might say, "You want a cookie?" when they want anything from a cookie to juice to a hug. Or they will learn only to request rather than to share and elaborate with caregivers. Both examples demonstrate the tendency toward the more concrete elements of speech. It is the more dynamic experiences of all aspects of communication that connect people and thoughts for long-term relationship health.

How to Talk Less

Talking less may mean using fewer words and more sound effects, gestures, and prosody (the singsong nature of our voices) to communicate. By talking less, you also declutter the auditory environment so that when you do talk, it can be more readily received. As a general rule, choose to only talk as much as your child or partner talks.

If you are trying to also expand language, often per speech pathologist recommendations, do so carefully. If you flood them with words, they will likely only digest the more concrete, literal, and verbal aspects. They may learn to repeat you but without curiosity about the other aspects of communication, such as sound effects, gestures, and environmental cues. They will miss the more subtle aspects of communication and habitually respond just to the more literal or concrete aspects.

If your child or partner is nonverbal, you should be interacting primarily with nonverbal communication—some sound effects and a couple of keywords. Consider looking up core vocabulary words, which are the words that carry great weight in communication, rather than individual labels, which are more limiting.

By talking less, you highlight the interaction between you, your presence, your collaboration. By talking less, you highlight the social engagement and relationship over concrete or static elements. Our communication with others and our relationship development is rooted not in literal, concrete words but in engagement and thought sharing. So generally speaking, if your child or partner is nonverbal, consider sound effects and single words. If your partner is using two-word phrases, but only once in a while, follow their lead on frequency. Add just one word or a sound effect to expand their language to three-word phrases. For example, your child or partner says, "Want train," and you say, "Oh! Red train!" or "Fast red train," or playfully, "Come here, train!" And if your child or partner is extremely adept at verbal communication but tends to not say much, allow more silence when you are together. Add in statements rather than potentially intimidating them or confusing things with too many open-ended questions.

If you notice that your child or partner is getting into a habit of repeating your model without gazing toward you for additional nonverbal communication, this shows that they are focusing on the concrete or static elements of speech. Take a step back. Highlight your social engagement and collaboration by choosing to stop talking. Developmentally, words come from social interaction—not the other way around. Using nonverbal communication and sound effects supports your child or partner in being a full, well-rounded, and effective communicator who's able to use more than just verbal communication to connect with those around them.

Earlier in my career, I was asked to speak with a group of adults on the spectrum about relationship development. One of my discussion points centered on the use of nonverbal communication. I offered an activity for them to do with a partner sitting next to them, and it required they do so without talking. At least a third of the participants became so anxious that they opted out of the activity. The activity was so severely anxiety-producing for them that they simply could not venture into the role-playing activity.

This taught me the power of practice to build confidence slowly but surely with nonverbal communication. The goal is that, as adults, they do not feel anxious and ill-prepared.

Autistic individuals are surrounded every day by verbal communicators who do not understand the sensory or emotional aspects of autism. The verbal communication also gets mixed in with the other sounds and noises around them. This can cause some people with autism to tune out and hyper-focus on concrete modes of communication out of self-preservation.

Or they might wait to tune out completely when they get home just to rejuvenate or recover. They may learn to respond only when they have to or if specifically directed to respond. The fullness of communication gets lost in the chaos of the day.

But you, as parents or supportive adults in a child's or partner's life, can counteract the chaos by simply reducing the overall amount you talk. This provides a soothing break from the auditory onslaught of the day while keeping the spotlight on the social engagement and nonverbal support and guidance you provide. You might even consider an hour after school or work (or during school if you are teacher or other professional) where you provide completely silent guidance. If a child or adult has learned that concrete verbal language and directives are the only way to communicate due to years of habit, it may be more challenging than you expect when you go nonverbal. They may request your voice return for safety and understanding. The good news is that if you start small, confidence and trust will build.

We tend to get into ruts of communicating primarily with directives, especially when someone seems resistant or needs more time for responding. Autistic people will tell us that they feel more comfortable simply being told what to do and not having to do the thinking, as this is commonly where their confidence is lacking. As previously noted, this is not ideal for their own development, thinking, and well-being.

Autism or not, children and teens all go through phases of wanting control and independence. It is normal for all humans to have a drive for what is called personal agency or control— having choice over their own lives. As Jonathan Chase shares in his book *From Surviving to Thriving*, if we are offering only directives, we leave the person with only two choices: to comply or not. To gain natural control and personal agency, they will choose to noncompliance.

We fall into patterns of nagging and cuing, and then we get frustrated that they do not do things without being told or that they show resistance to doing anything we ask at all. We want them to clean their rooms and exercise, take charge of homework and appointments, and make and keep friends. As a result, they either get stuck passively complying—which feels great for you as a parent until you want them to do it without being asked—or the opposite happens, and they get stuck actively resisting.

If we are primarily providing a child, teen, or adult with directives, we are not giving them opportunities for free choice and personal agency. In addition, people who feel out of control or who lack opportunities for personal agency will take control in ways that may not work for them or the people around them. It's when someone takes this maladaptive control that we see challenging behaviors: an individual who is feeling backed into a corner and wants to exert their independence may do so by running away, yelling mean things at people, falling to the floor, hitting, biting, or using other expressions of anger or frustration. Other people with autism may not push back on your directives and demand their own personal agency. But it is still our job to provide opportunities so that they realize their own power over their actions, choices, and lives.

Move from Fixing to Coaching

When we try to fix situations for our children or partners with autism, we remove their personal agency and reinforce learned helplessness. This can be an unconscious yet continual and habitual blow to their self-esteem and self-worth.

While it may feel well-meaning to remove obstacles before your child or partner sees them, you are also removing the opportunity for growth and confidence-building. When someone struggles with decision-making, it is not our job to jump in to fix the problems. It is our job to provide them time, opportunities, and coaching instead.

Everyday life is full of many mini opportunities for decision-making. We decide what to wear, when to eat, where to sit, what to watch on TV, and more. Be cognizant of the overwhelm factor we discussed in chapter 2. If you offer multiple opportunities above and beyond their capability, you run the risk of reducing their self-esteem by offering opportunities outside of their zone of ability or zone of proximal development. When you offer opportunities in very small but powerful ways and within their zone, you meet them where they are while raising their own expectations of themselves. By reducing your overall verbal communication, you can turn your simplified wording into opportunities or challenges that lead to personal agency. Of course, you may have to adjust to your child or partner's receptive communication level.

Directing or Fixing	Coaching
"Come here."	"I need your help."
"Turn on the light."	"It's dark in here."
"Get the forks from the drawer."	"Uh-oh, I forgot the forks."
"Give me that one."	"Oh, that one looks fun."
"Did you remember to X?"	"I think you might have forgotten something."
Jumping in to tell them to do something before they even see the problem (e.g., telling them to ask you for help, giving them the solution to fix the issue).	Pausing and allowing your child or partner to witness the problem and experiment with fixes or ask for your help.

A way to know you are moving from fixing to coaching is to observe the individual's response. I'd rather you observe their response rather than getting too hyper-focused on exactly what you say. If you ask questions that have single correct answers and the individual quickly responds without much thought, you are not providing a choice but solely an opportunity for compliance or noncompliance. I call this "mindless communication" versus our goal of "mindful communication." For example, if you ask, "What is it?" and point at something, there is only one answer you are looking for; for example, the item's label. Similarly, if you ask a yes-or-no question, you are only looking for compliance or noncompliance.

Consider asking more open-ended questions that are adjusted to your partner's level of understanding. If the person struggles significantly with making their own choices, consider starting with just two or three choices. You may ask them if they'd like an apple or snack bar, for example. If your child or partner is ready for more, consider providing three to four choices or go as far as experimenting with completely open-ended questions in familiar situations. You may ask them if they'd like an apple, snack bar, or popcorn, but as they are more and more successful with the three choices, you can bump up your question to "What would you like to eat for a snack?"

Slow Down and Agree on the Problem

When we jump in to fix things too soon, we also remove the person's opportunity to recognize that there is even a problem to fix. At the moment that you offer a solution to a problem, they may not have even shifted their attention to the issue at hand yet—and you are already on to fixing it.

The first step is to slow down to identify the problem along with your child or partner. Agree upon the problem before moving too quickly into solving it. If you choose to swoop in and solve something for someone, you run the serious risk of solving something that wasn't even the primary issue for the person. This will swiftly lead you into a rabbit hole of misunderstanding and miscalculations.

Recently, I guided a couple to agree with their son regarding various issues before jumping in to "solve mode" too soon. They were and had been very clear that the problem to solve was that their young adult son was being too loud in public and wouldn't quiet down when requested to do so. They amped up their efforts to get him to stop, and his loudness simply got worse. He became even more rigid about stopping. They were stuck in a loop.

I guided them to consider that the problem they were trying to solve—his being loud—may not be the right problem to solve. He had a different problem: of wanting to be independent and exert his voice loudly. When the problem was properly determined—that he was being loud out of frustration and a lack of independence—they were able to consider other situations when he could be free of directives and corrections, such as on the running track and certain times of day at home. This alleviated the loud and forceful situations on their walks together, as they had respected his need for independence and personal agency elsewhere.

Multidimensional Problem Solving

Many years ago, a colleague pulled me aside to lecture me on the fact that individuals with autism process problems in a very one-dimensional manner. She described the autistic experience of seeing a problem and determining only one solution to said problem. Her target was compliance, and she explained that the solution they choose is commonly maladjusted. For example, they may hit whenever they want something. They may isolate themselves whenever they feel anxious or overwhelmed. They may go into static verbal loops of saying a phrase over and over again, thinking that repetition will make them feel less anxious.

In my opinion, while my colleague was spot-on in some ways, she wanted me as a professional to teach to that manner of decision-making without trying to help them think more dynamically and more independently. She instructed me to assume that this is simply the way their brains work, and we must teach to their static way of learning.

Many well-meaning professionals teach to this one-directional way of problem solving by redirecting to new, better single-use fixes. For example, if a child is hitting when frustrated, the professional or parent may give that child something to hit that is safe, or they may teach that child to say "I'm frustrated" instead. This makes sense and can certainly be useful for short-term fixes, and teaching in this manner is the basis of many behavioral programs that are commonplace in our autism communities now. The reason for or function of a certain behavior is determined, and you find an alternative to that behavior that can work better in the long term for that child or person. Then you reinforce their use of that behavior. Again, this is an excellent approach for some things, but not everything. And it sets the bar pretty low for people with autism to learn to think for themselves.

Where I feel that my colleague and many current interventionists go wrong is assuming that people with autism cannot consider multiple solutions and learn to think for themselves. If we stop at one-dimensional problem solving, we deprive the individual of the opportunities to be found in learning to observe a problem and select from a number of options for responding. This is truly living and having true personal agency. If we want something, we must be able to make decisions depending on the environment and other people.

Here's an example of one-dimensional problem solving. If we give a person on the spectrum the understanding that every time they want something, they have to ask for it using the exact phrase, "I want _____," the solution will fall flat. It will leave them quite frustrated in many social situations, like when they want a turn with a ball on the playground or a doughnut in the employee lounge.

By bringing autistic individuals into the problem-solving conversation earlier, we can provide opportunities for the person to learn to experiment with their own solutions to problems. They can recognize that they have the choice and opportunity to select which one works best for them in a given situation. Please consider referring back to the Sun Diagram described in chapters 3 and 5 for offering solutions for a person to consider. In this diagram, the problem is depicted in the center of the sun, and each ray coming out from the center represents an option for solving that same problem. Using this diagram with people on the spectrum can often be a helpful visual and can assist them in understanding that they have options. Again, each person is completely different, so some people may not need or want the visual, or they may not need it once the concept is understood.

One young person I worked with would become anxious every time her brother made noise in the house, such as yelling or playing loudly. The family used the Sun Diagram to offer choices for what she could do when this happened.

The parents sat down with her and a piece of paper one day when she was calm. They ensured that she had her attention and curiosity shifted to their conversation rather than something she was thinking about or something she was seeing on the TV or another screen. They shared that they noticed that she would get upset when her brother made noises in the house. They drew the circle in the middle of the page with a grumpy-looking face in the center. Then they drew one ray coming out of the sun's center. At the end of that one ray, they wrote what she currently does: screaming "Shut up!"

They took it slow and guided the conversation in a very nonjudgmental, matter-of-fact way. They then offered the fact that there are other rays and other ways of solving the same problem. They drew another ray and shared that she could go to her room and close the door. (They wrote "room with door closed," but you could draw a door for someone less verbal). Then they drew another ray and shared that she could put her noise-cancelling headphones on.

They added another ray and offered her the opportunity to share a solution they might not have thought of. She offered, "Tell you to tell him to shut up." This gave them the opportunity to revise that option, with her input, to her asking them for help, which was a great option.

They ended up with several options, including going outside in the backyard, covering her ears, singing a song to herself, breathing deeply, and simply learning to ignore the noises. When she used other options on the Sun Diagram, she was celebrated for them by having extra time with one of her parents each Friday by herself.

CHAPTER 11

Creating Partnerships

*The experience of many of us is not that
"insistence on sameness" jumps out unbidden and
unwanted and makes our lives hard, but that
"insistence on sameness" is actually a way of
adapting to a confusing and chaotic environment.*
—Dr. Dora Raymaker

As humans, we all start our early development with the nice, easy, back-and-forth gazing with our caregivers that we now know is called "social reciprocity." This back-and-forth gazing gives way to games like peekaboo and tickle games. Later we expand into more sophisticated games and conversations. The complexity of the social reciprocity changes and increases over time and with experience. All of our positive-feeling little social moments, games, and conversations have the elements of partnerships. Partnerships with loved ones help us develop healthy attachments, learn new things from our teachers and peers, and form deep bonds with those we love and care about.

If you think about a time when you really connected with someone, you may have been sharing an activity like a conversation or doing something together. You may have shared ideas and memories. You most likely had a reciprocity between you that felt comfortable, enticing, or intriguing. This experience, at its core, is a partnership and includes what is called "joint attention." For further discussion on joint attention, please refer to chapter 1, "The Cascade Effect."

When partnering with an infant, you make a sound, and they gaze back at you. When you make another sound, they may make a sound back. Then you switch it up a little and may act silly, and they smile. The child responds with a smile or coo for you. You as caregiver then naturally offer another smile or coo. If the infant responds to the smile or coo with a sad face or grimace, you would respond with comfort by offering a sad face back or choosing to make soothing sounds. At the core of these actions is a partnership where each partner has a role, and they are responsive to one another.

As a child develops, they are able to engage in partnerships at much more complex levels, including adding objects and toys. We call this ability to engage with both a person and an object or topic "joint attention." In autism, we are learning that when this complexity is added, the child is not able to actively engage in the back-and-forth of joint attention and social reciprocity at the same level as typically developing peers. As we know, autism is a spectrum. Some children will completely retreat from the social reciprocity and focus almost exclusively on toys or objects, not developing speech and staying nonverbal.

Other children will engage in some back-and-forth and learn language that is more one-sided or topic-centric rather than complex and incorporating the thoughts and ideas of others.

Social reciprocity with joint attention is essential for full, well-rounded development. Again, please refer to chapter 1 for full details on the importance of social reciprocity. It is through these trusted early partnerships that we develop the attachment that is used as our safe harbor, as Dr. Tina Payne-Bryson and Dr. Daniel Siegel shared in their book, *The Power of Showing Up*. The child knows that the intimate partnership between themselves and their primary care provider is solid, trustworthy, and can be referenced in moments of uncertainty. Throughout life we engage with others regarding toys, objects, and interests, soaking in their attitudes to tell us what items or topics we should accept, reject, or explore further.

Partnering Defined

I am using the term "partnership" as shorthand for the framework we use to practice social reciprocity at any age. Partnerships are essential for the lasting connections we make with peers who we later call friends.

We may, for instance, partner in play while building with Lego bricks in class. You notice that within the partnership, they respect our space as much as we need, and you in turn respect theirs. You hand them a Lego when they seem to be looking for one. They hand you a Lego they think we may be looking for as well. Fast-forward to the lunchroom at work. You may notice someone wearing a sweatshirt with your favorite team's logo on it. You offer a thumbs-up as they walk in the door. They smile and ask, "You like this team?" and you answer, "Have since I was a kid." The conversation continues for a few more turns back and forth in a comfortable rhythm that makes you feel like you may just become friends.

You feel closer to someone who responds to your bids in a contingent and related manner. You feel closer to someone who reads your nonverbal cues and takes action accordingly. You feel closer to those you can gain a partnership with by using words or movements.

The reverse of this shared Lego example is the child who becomes upset when someone even comes near the Lego, fearful that the other person may move their structure or take valued bricks. And the reverse of the lunchroom scenario is that the person looks confused without saying anything when their coworker comments on the team logo. The bid for connection is dropped, and a partnership is not formed.

This social partnering is essential for what is called "social referencing." The child learns the value of sizing up their caregiver's or peers' interests or opinions for safety. They look to their parents prior to crossing the street—learning what the parent is looking for and why. The child who is adept at social reciprocity with their parent or caregiver actively engages in activities alongside them to better understand the world. This is why we see children with strong social reciprocity development imitating caregivers by engaging in daily life activities, such as talking on the phone or trying foods their caregivers find tasty.

In autism, the gaze to and the curiosity for the caregiver's perspective is impacted. As mentioned in chapter 1, expert researchers in the field suspect that the child's initiation of joint attention is the key issue that seems to thwart this mode of learning. I call the initiation aspect of joint attention Curiosity to You or C2U. This early social partnering and curiosity to others is essential for feeling successful in relationships. It is also the very core of autism. We can provide accommodations and opportunities for people on the autism spectrum to partner with us in ways that will help them both practice and feel valued.

I don't know about you, but I am much more comfortable at a party or a big gathering of people if I have a job to do or a role to play. I will find something to do to help whenever possible—not necessarily because I am altruistic, but because I know that it will help me manage the social chaos of big groups. Children in classrooms often jostle to be line leader or to bring the attendance sheet to the office. We all like to feel helpful. We like to have roles within social engagements. People with autism may not initiate, let alone fight for, a job or role, but they thrive like the rest of us when it is given to them. They also appreciate and find the concreteness of roles and being told what to do stress-relieving.

The adult child living at home is almost always very willing and compliant when given a task or chore to do. But goodness, parents get frustrated with what seems like a serious lack of initiative. People with autism may not initiate their own roles, and they may miss social nuances, which subsequently leads to low confidence. If we offer clear and easy roles for them within everyday life, they can learn to initiate while gaining confidence in social engagements. By partnering in everyday situations like cooking or taking out the garbage together, you can give that person practice negotiating and coordinating movements, reading your facial expressions, and bringing their best selves to relationships. When someone truly learns something, they have digested it, practiced it, and found their confidence with it. Then generalizing that behavior toward peers becomes easier and more natural. The goals on so many educational plans for "taking turns with peers" will be a thing of the past.

Practicing Partnering

When we partner, we learn to read the other person's verbal and nonverbal cues to determine if our initiations and responses are contingent with theirs. We learn to read the other person's preferences through their actions as well as their reactions to us. We must engage our visual systems, our bodies, and our minds to negotiate moment by moment what our partner's communication is telling us and how we might respond. We prioritize information from our partners rapidly, figuring out what information to ignore and what information is most important to you and to them.

Partnering is just as it sounds—two or more people sharing the responsibility for a task or activity. For infants, this can look like the examples I mentioned earlier: peekaboo or tickle games. But as a child grows, it can look like cleaning up toys together or setting the table together. Each of the partners takes at least 50% of the responsibility for the activity to happen and continue.

I will often have people start out with very brief, one-time partnering tasks, such as opening a bag of chips together or working together to open or close a bottle of juice. As you become increasingly comfortable with partnering, you can focus on extending the length of time you engage together in the partnership. This will mean choosing longer activities with repeated opportunities, like washing something together, eating something together out of the same container, playing a game together, or doing a chore together.

In the appendix, I have provided a list of common, everyday activities you can potentially use for partnering practice with someone you know with autism. Consider putting it up on your refrigerator or wall and checking off those you use as practice.

Challenges You May Face

I would like to share some of the reasons why it may be challenging to put partnering into practice with someone with autism. Having an understanding of why partnering can be difficult will help you relax in the moment and not take things personally.

Challenges depend on a person's age and experiences. A child without a strong grasp of partnering has learned to grow primarily when they are in full control and are comfortable. Anything outside of their own personal control will feel uncharted, unpredictable, and anxiety provoking. They will need you as their partner to go slow and take small steps into this uncharted territory with them while they gain trust in you, themselves, and their competency in social partnering.

Autistic individuals may have had situations where they have reached out to others to actively engage but were met with responses that they did not expect. An example might be trying to engage with fellow students at school but being bullied in response. They may shut down or discontinue the interactions, but so often they continue trying and continue to get hurt. They've determined erroneously that social partnering and the unpredictability that comes with it are not helpful to their learning and may not be pleasant at all.

Partnering practice requires learning how to respond to unpredictable bids from others in a contingent manner. This is no small task for any of us, and the reality is that we engage in a lot of trial and error throughout our social lives. By partnering, you will help the person with autism learn resiliency and the ability to roll with the unexpected responses from others in their lives. The hope is that they'll find these unexpected responses intriguing or enjoyable rather than overwhelming and unmotivating.

You see, partnering comes naturally for many of us. We may be introverts or less social than others, but the ability to partner is deeply ingrained in our development. We use partnering for many different aspects of life. We take action to help others. We may see someone struggle with opening a door and rush to their aid—partnering with them naturally to complete their intended goal of opening the door. We notice when someone drops something, and we stoop to pick it up and return it to them. As children we play with other children, creating friendships by taking turns and creating imaginary worlds together in partnerships. And as teens and adults, we meet others who we fall in love with through the dance we call "social reciprocity," or more simply, partnerships.

Even early in development, we engage with our primary caregivers in partnerships that involve gazing that then gives rise to more complexity as we grow. We add emotions, objects, and words to the interactions. From these early partnerships, we learn such things as:

- What is safe or unsafe
- What is interesting and not
- Ways we might expand our play
- The names of things
- How to get our needs met
- The interests and actions of others

If we don't have this early foundation of skilled part-nering, or if it is stilted in any way, a child becomes limited in how they can learn effectively and efficiently. They can still learn from their own exploration—their brains will still grow and develop—but it will be different. The child may seek sameness (such as wanting the same pink cup night after night or for you to drive a certain way to get to the store) rather than feel comfortable with unpredictability. This is because they have not learned how to manage un-certainty within the partnering engagements with caregivers. They may seek routines and rituals (eating the same foods, playing with toys in the same way, playing video games or movies repetitively) rather than seeking people for comfort and regulation. They have not learned to "coregulate" with others through these early partnerships, so they may have regulation needs. Children learn to regulate their own neu-robiological systems by borrowing the calm that their care-givers bring to the partnership. Picture a caregiver rocking an upset baby to soothe them.

We naturally partner with our caregivers early in development—as in peekaboo or even walking our first steps while holding someone's hands. For people with autism, this partnering for social development may happen then stop, or not happen at all, or simply be significantly delayed while other aspects of development stay seemingly on track. This can be confusing for parents and loved ones when other areas are developing at a faster rate. We tend to ask ourselves, "If they can do this, why can't they do that?" A very young child may be able to use a key to open a lock. Another may be able to recall facts from history that astonish those around them. And another may memorize and recite car license plate numbers. It is the social reciprocity that is delayed and changes the trajectory of their development. So if we remember this key aspect of autism rather than get frustrated with the person for not "acting their age," we can build rather than dismantle their fragile confidence. Believe me, I know from my clients that the child, teen, or adult is already asking themselves, "If I can do all of these other things, why can't I be successful socially?" We do not need to help them question their abilities any more than they already do. Our job is to help them build their confidence rather than tear it down.

Partnering mindfully with someone with autism will raise their confidence and their feelings of being understood and seen. They may not have had someone who understood how to partner with them before. You don't have to teach partnering as a discrete skill. I find that one of the beautiful things about partnering with someone with autism is that all you have to do is *allow* the opportunity for the person to engage in partnerships by adjusting the speed and complexity level so that it works for them. You might think of it as a muscle that has not been activated, or not activated enough to be particularly useful. The person will be hesitant to use that muscle, then need small amounts of practice to slowly build it up, before they are able to partner fluidly and with confidence. It will take time and diligence for both of you.

People with autism are commonly considered black-and-white thinkers. Being a black-and-white thinker is another way of saying that someone sees the concrete or literal aspects of activities. They may see a situation such as emptying the dishwasher as a solo activity. In their mind, it does not require two people. They may even determine it is more efficient to do alone. While you may consider emptying it together fun, rewarding, efficient, or a bonding activity, they may not see it that way. Keep trying. Keep offering. Sometimes just asking or mentioning why it is meaningful to you can plant the seed for natural partnering to happen later. They might eventually, spontaneously involve you in emptying the dishwasher without your having to ask. Sometimes the first response of "no" is a way that they afford themselves processing time. When you ask again, they are ready to join you.

Still other people with autism are overwhelmed, or they have developed significant habits or fears around partnering. They may have tried so many times on the playground, in class, with you, and with others that they are burned out on trying. You may have to take it very slowly to regain trust. They may have built up ways to protect themselves before overwhelm happens. They can control the amount of uncertainty they have to experience by saying no when invited into a partnership.

One of my clients is a twelve-year-old who is very savvy with computers and games, and he can build the most involved structures out of almost anything. When I try to partner with him outright by saying something like, "Let's do this together," he moans. When I push it, he will outright refuse.

I have had to go very slowly and offer partnering opportunities within the topics and activities where he already feels confident. We have built numerous Lego structures, which he can do with incredible speed and accuracy. We have built and played with racecar ramps and systems, complete with corkscrew turns and cars flying off the tracks. I have had to insert myself in very small ways at first and then increase my active participation with him to fifty-fifty. And even still, it feels like we take three steps forward together on some days and other times, two steps back.

Wait until They Are Ready

One of my favorite things to say when I am engaging with someone with autism is "I'll wait until you are ready." What I mean by this is that I will stay poised to listen if they need a bit more time to process what they would like to say, shift their attention, or simply gather their thoughts. We are so quick, especially in Western culture, to jump in and fill the silence. But with people with autism, this may completely negate their ability to share and initiate within conversations. Additionally, when we assume a child who is nonverbal has nothing to say, we take away the opportunity for them to share their thinking with us. The nonverbal child who puts things together swiftly and easily, or the nonverbal adult who lights up when you watch food shows, can share their interests if you are just curious enough to listen.

As I hope it is now very clear, significant sensory and attention-shifting needs can make social connections and learning extremely challenging. A person with autism may seek familiar and repetitive patterns in an attempt to soothe themselves. They may retreat to their room for video gaming or get into verbal loops that are repetitive. These may be attempts for them to regulate when stressed or to engage when lonely. By providing a framework or an outline for successful engagements, you can help them both regulate and engage socially more successfully.

How to Partner

People with autism are all beautifully unique and different from one another. All of us have our own personalities, inner lives, experiences, and families, including autistics. The similarity between people with the diagnosis of autism is that they have this fundamental challenge to social reciprocity (or partnering) and restricted or repetitive interests for behaviors. I would be extremely remiss to try to tell you there was one way to partner with every human with autism. It will depend on their interests, their personalities, their age, and their previous experiences.

Once your partner is comfortable with the outline of your partnerships, you can start experimenting with moments of uncertainty—moments you can play with that make you stand out over the toy, object, or topic of conversation that you're sharing. Remember when I talked about how we want to stay in the person's zone of proximal development, where they are at their best for learning? We do not want to bore them with partnering that doesn't change or expand, but we also do not want to overwhelm them by offering too much silliness or over-exaggeration that turns them away from the interaction.

To help get you started, I am going to recommend steps by age. But remember that the true art of partnering is in your willingness to experiment—so do not skip the next section on practice!

PARTNERING WITH AN INFANT

Having a primary adult who is caring for them in sensitive ways, one who can perceive, make sense of, and respond to their needs, gives them a feeling of safety. The sense of well-being that emerges from predictable and repeated experiences of care creates what the attachment theory pioneer John Bowlby called a "secure base."

—Dr. Daniel J. Siegel and Mary Hartzell

Partnering with an infant can be a beautiful back-and-forth that guides you to understand one another so that secure attachment can be developed. This is how you can engage the child in a relaxed back-and-forth gazing exercise:

1. Orient your child in your lap facing you, or face them while they are in a supportive chair of some sort. Make sure the environment is quiet and you are not distracted.
2. You look to them; they look to you.

3. Then you change something about how you are gazing at them. Maybe you smile. Maybe you look surprised. Maybe you look up or down. You do something that is slightly different in the back-and-forth between you.

4. You allow the infant the time to adjust and shift their attention to you. You do not chase their gaze.

5. Continue in this manner for at least three or four "laps" (back and forth is equal to one lap).

6. Stop the interaction while the two of you are enjoying it rather than waiting for your child to tire of the social game. Leave your child wanting more without depriving them in the moment.

7. Be sure to practice several times per day—especially if your child is not initiating it on their own. If they are initiating it on their own, that is a good sign that they are finding it comforting and rewarding.

Here's another way to do partnering if your infant or young child is engaging with toys or objects. In this type of partnering session, you are giving the child an opportunity to realize their role in a social interaction. Their role is to take the item. Then you are giving the child an opportunity to realize their own personal agency or personal choice by allowing them to do whatever they choose to do with the item. And you give them practice with engaging in a contingent manner with your actions. Here's how it works:

1. You hand them a toy or item.

2. They take the toy to chew, manipulate, toss, or throw.

3. You then might change in very small, manageable ways

how you hand the item to the child. You may add silly sounds or actions.

A very important note: Remember that at any point, if your partner or child seems distressed or anxious, make the partnership immediately simple with fewer words or sounds. Bring down the chaos of sensory input. Bring it back to the basic outline of your engagement. Simply hand items to them with no or very little noise, distractions, words, or complexity.

PARTNERING WITH A TODDLER

Partnering with a toddler can be fun and playful, as they are usually quite amenable to your ideas.

1. Offer mini moments to partner within your daily routine or within play. These can be great practice for your child in engaging in social reciprocity and partnering.
2. Try to mix it up and join their play as much as you invite them into your play and activities. Join them in their play even if it seems very solitary. Start by sitting near and slowly adding new or slightly different elements as you engage. You might put your hand out and wait for them to give you an item from their play, which turns into a nice partnership of their supplying you with toys to then manipulate. You also may choose to play with similar toys in a parallel manner, or even add imaginary elements they may not have thought of yet. The key is to observe and be sure not to overwhelm at any point. Add something mindfully and with the mindset that you are

seeking to share control and partner without either of you dominating. Similarly, you can invite them to put towels in the dryer, for example, or help you wash a window, set the table, stir the cookie dough, or put ingredients into a recipe. Each of these chore-type activities can be quite fun with a toddler, especially if you are not in a hurry.

3. Each time it is your turn within the partnership, or as you are actively partnering, add little changes or variations so that it is not always the same—but also not too overwhelming for your child. Be sure to consider that window of tolerance, green zone, or river of well-being for them. Challenge them in nudges rather than pushing them over the edge, into the bank of the river, or outside their window of tolerance.

4. If you go too far, your child may resist or insist on sameness. Simply ratchet it back a little and try again.

5. Try to never end on a frustrated note but rather a successful note, even if you have to make your partnership easy at the end of your activity together. Your child will build resilience and confidence in social engagement by your small yet manageable additions to your social engagement practice.

6. Practice several times per day by following their lead and by guiding them into activities you would like to do as well. Balance who starts the activity, in other words.

PARTNERING WITH A YOUNG CHILD

Partnering with a three- to five-year-old can be very similar to partnering with a toddler. Additionally, once a child is in this age range, they may have started to build up some resistance to partnering and the social engagement we wish to practice. They may find comfort in sameness and see your variations as overwhelming or simply not interesting. Therefore they may be less likely to accept the invitation into partnering with you.

Try not to take it personally. Remember, this is the core issue of autism. Social reciprocity is neurologically challenging for them. They have built up great coping strategies to avoid interactions where they are not as strong or confident. Go slowly and follow your child's lead into play at this age.

1. Sit next to them while they are playing on their own. Allow them to see you as an observer rather than someone who is going to change their play. For some children this may take a few days of practice on its own.

2. When your child seems fine with this observation, you can slowly and deliberately touch your child or the toys while they are playing. I am not implying that you "mess" with their toys or touch them in a rough or inappropriate manner. Simply add your presence by touching the toy gently and letting go, or by touching your child's shoulder gently for a moment then let go. This establishes you as a safe person who will and can enter their space without overwhelming them. This may be as far as you go for a full week of practice. Allow that time. You are not in a hurry. If you hurry, you will overwhelm the child—guaranteed. You have nothing to lose by going slow at this stage and focusing on building trust.

3. You'll know you have established a gentle touch of either their shoulder or toy as being okay when your child stays relaxed and engaged with their activity. Then you can

move on to making very small offers of engagement. You may put your hand out and hold it there near your child's toys. Or you may push a block closer to them. None of these are paired with any words, sound effects, or enthusiasm yet. Save those for later. Right now, you are building trust that your additions and partnering with them will not be overwhelming but enjoyable and intriguing. You are piquing and fostering their curiosity about you, which I call Curiosity to You or C2U.

4. Next, offer partnering by giving them a block or toy that adds to their play—but still no words or sound effects yet. Allow this stage to be comfortable and relaxed before moving on.

5. Now you can offer sound effects or words paired with your actions in play. Again, go slowly, and observe your child's response. If sounds or words seem to agitate them, stop talking or making sound effects. Go back a step. If the sounds or words seem intriguing, however, keep playing with them as you ratchet up your additions a bit each time—as long as your child stays engaged, comfortable, and intrigued. Always end on an easy, not-as-exciting addition to your partnering. Remember, leave them wanting more and not in a frustrated state whenever possible.

6. As you both become comfortable with partnering, you will start to do it more often. Try to ensure that you provide partnering in both play and chore-like activities, including those led by you and by them. You want a balance of each.

PARTNERING WITH AN OLDER CHILD

Once a child is bit older, they start establishing routines and habits of interacting (or not). They also have more people they must interact with at home, at school, and in the community. And they may have more experience with interactions *not* working by this point than with those that do work for them. They may be more wary to engage, especially if the topic of engagement—a game, a toy, or a conversation—is not eliciting or focusing on one of their strengths.

Their extra challenges surrounding interactions does not mean they are not capable. It simply means they may need extra practice and more confidence-building while or perhaps before targeting partnering or social reciprocity.

1. On day one of partnering with your child, sit next to them when they are playing on their own. Allow them to see you as an observer rather than someone who is going to change their play. You may be simply sitting on the couch next to them while they are playing a video game. You may be sitting on the floor near them while they are building something.

2. When your child seems fine with your being close by without interaction, you can slowly and deliberately touch your child or the toys while they are playing. Only touch them—don't manipulate the toys or objects or attempt to get any response. Be genuinely curious without being a threat to their solitary play. Add your presence by touching the toy gently and letting go, or by touching your child's shoulder gently but firmly for a moment, then letting go. Do this as if you are just observing the

pieces and putting them down again. This establishes you as a safe person who will and can enter their space without overwhelming them. This may be as far as you go for a full week of practice. Allow that time. You are not in a hurry. If you hurry, you will overwhelm your child—guaranteed. You have nothing to lose by going slow at this stage and focusing on trust building. The goal is trust, not to get your child to do anything in particular and certainly not to overstress the child into anger or upset of any kind.

3. Once you have established that gently touching or touching their toys seems to be okay—meaning your child stays relaxed and engaged with their activity—then you can move on to offering small "bids" for engagement. Think of these bids as very small invitations to partner. So you may put your hand out and hold it there near your child's toys. Or you may push a block closer to them. None of these are paired with any words, sound effects, or enthusiasm yet. Save those for later. Right now, you are building trust that your additions and partnering with them will not be overwhelming but enjoyable.

4. Next, offer partnering by giving them a block or toy that adds to their play, still without words or sound effects. Allow this stage to be comfortable and relaxed before moving on.

5. The next step is to offer sound effects or words paired with your actions in play. Again, go slowly, and observe your child's response. If sounds or words seem to agitate them, stop talking or making sound effects. Go back a step. If the sounds or words are intriguing, however,

keep playing with them as you ratchet up your additions a bit each time. Stay with it as long as your child stays engaged, comfortable, and intrigued. Always end on an easy, not-as-exciting addition to your partnering. Remember, leave them wanting more and not in a frustrated state whenever possible.

6. As you both become comfortable with partnering, you will start to do it more often. Try to ensure that you provide partnering in both play and chore-like activities, including those led by you and by them. You want a balance of each.

It is essential by this point to ensure that you are able to both follow their lead in play as much as they can follow you into and within activities. This provides your child with active engagement and practice in sharing control. Being able to share control is extremely important when learning to interact with others. You are more likely to make friends when you are competent at sharing materials as well as responsibilities. Here are steps for guiding your child to follow you into your play or lifestyle activity:

1. Approach your child in a nonconfrontational manner. This may mean staying quiet and not using words. It may also mean getting to your child's eye level or below.

2. Allow your child's attention to shift from whatever they are doing or thinking about at the time to you and your presence. This is what I call Curiosity to You, or C2U for short. Do not assume that your child can shift their

attention as soon as you enter the room and start talking. They may need time to shift their curiosity and attention to you first.

3. Once you observe through their body language that their attention and curiosity has shifted to you, they are ready for you to talk or state your intention: "It's time for lunch," or "I need your help." Your child still may balk at the transition, as many children might. But allowing their attention to shift will allow them to hear you and comply more readily rather than simply fighting their understanding and potential overwhelm right from the start.

4. Your child may start to come with you and then decide otherwise. This often happens in the first few days of working on transitions in this manner. All you have to do is restart this process. Be nonconfrontational, stay quiet, allow attention to shift, and restate where you are intending to go. Do not rush this. Allow your child to join you of their own volition; do not carry or force your child to the next location. This takes away what is called their "personal agency," which we wish to strengthen.

5. If your child flops to the floor, you can offer your hand and a slight pull toward you (*not* aggressively, just slight tension applied in the direction of standing up). If your child fights this, let go. Offer the other hand and keep your clear stance of moving toward the intended target, but slow down. Allow some back-and-forth that may even become playful. Your child has come back online with you and will join you in the transition. Again, you may have to do this several times, either days in a row

or even simply on the way to one location. It will get better. Stay calm, cool, and collected as the guide. Clearly indicate that you will give time, but you are moving in that direction eventually.

PARTNERING WITH A TEEN OR YOUNG ADULT

Partnering with a teen or young adult is wonderful yet takes a different approach from any of the above. Your teen or young adult not only has set habits and routines surrounding social engagement, but they also are at an age when they are naturally less interested in partnering with their parents for much of anything. That said, most of the autistic teens and young adults I have met are incredibly kind-natured if you find ways to connect first about their topics of interest.

The steps to partner with them are similar to the steps to partner with an older child, but there are slight differences.

1. Establish a routine time with your teen or young adult when you do not need anything from them. This is a time when you are not going to nag, request, or lecture them. You are just there to be with them. It may take longer than you think for your teen or adult to feel comfortable sharing that space with you in this first step. Your teen or young adult may be so used to people around them only connecting with them when they need something or have done something wrong that they avoid it. They've probably learned simply to stay away or decline invitations.

2. As you are establishing your downtime together, also establish times in which you can be at your most curious

about your teen's or young adult's interests. This is a time when you can let go of your own agenda and truly attempt to understand why your teen or adult is intrigued by the things that at other times may annoy you. This is a time when you ask questions about their specific topics of interests or, if your teen or young adult is nonverbal or minimally verbal, engage in the activities that bring them joy.

3. During this time, bring in what you learned in chapter 9, "Getting Curious." Ask questions and make comments, but by all means, be authentic. This is not a time to attempt or pretend to make them think you are interested in participating in their thing. You need to find a place in yourself where you truly can be curious. If you simply cannot be in this mindset, find another topic or interest you share where you can.

4. Once you have established an interest, look for tiny openings where you can engage in a partnership with the interest or activity. For example, if a teen or young adult is intrigued by characters in a card game, play that card game. Have them teach you how. If they are interested in history, consider sharing a fact from history each night at dinner. If they are politically minded, watch a show then actively debate the issues together. You may wish to set ground rules.

5. Once you have established routines for steps 1 and 2 above (do not skip those steps), you can move on to giving your teen or young adult a choice of two options for something you'd like to do together. You might ask, "Would you like to have dinner together or take a walk

together?" Giving a choice within a nonchoice will support their natural need for control and foster personal agency while remaining clear about your expectation for them to join you in something. During the activity that was chosen, take very small steps to partner with them. You might carry something to the car together, put groceries away together, empty the dishwasher as a team, or walk together while keeping pace with one another.

Please note that while partnering may be incredibly easy for some, it may be quite challenging for your partner. You may have to make minor accommodations at first. You can always build complexity as your and your partner's confidence grows.

PARTNERING WITH A FULLY GROWN ADULT

Very similar to the teen and young adult steps for partnering, partnering with a fully grown adult may take the form of sharing their special interests to gain trust and build up the partnering concept. This may take the form of video gaming, watching scary movies together, or playing Magic: The Gathering. Whatever the special interest, try to find ways to partner with them around their specialized topics. If they monologue about a specific topic, you might invite them to show you their favorite websites, or demonstrate something, or draw something with you. These activities bring in a physically active component, not just mental participation between you.

Being listened to by someone can be the greatest "therapy" or intervention of its own accord. We all need to be seen and accepted for who we are as humans. So if you spend all of your time pushing those interests aside in favor of interventions, fixing, or changing the person, they will continue to feel depressed and less confident.

My own partner for seven years was most likely on the autism spectrum. It was not natural or habitual for him to partner in chores or activities with me—but he could. I had to specifically ask, and honestly, it tired me sometimes to have to ask. Sometimes I just wanted him to join me naturally without my having to ask. At times he would be involved in a task that seemed like it would go faster or be more efficient with my help. I would be right there ready, and it wouldn't even seem to cross his mind to involve me to make his job easier and more enjoyable.

I did understand his processing and tendency to think that solitary pursuits seemed easier than collaborating. And when we did partner in something, it was always very rewarding. It did usually need to be set up, and it was commonly out of my comfort zone, but when I got it right, it was awesome.

And it often spurred more opportunities for partnering since it felt good for both of us. We played complicated strategy-based board games together. Where I had in the past enjoyed board games for the social elements, I learned to enjoy the mental challenges they presented. We played video games on occasion, and he even tried to find a game or two he thought I'd enjoy playing together with him. That said, my lack of years of agility with the controllers made me a very undesirable partner for any speed or actual winning. We would sometimes cook together. He was very precise in his cooking, so it was necessary for us to determine roles ahead of time and for us to stay in our lanes while cooking.

There was not much wiggle room for adding any suspense or plot twists, which you will read about in the next chapter. Emptying the dishwasher together started hilariously, as I was ready to partner immediately when I first moved in, and he announced I was in his way—until I specifically said that I enjoyed doing chores with him and we could get it done more quickly. After I pushed my agenda, he even stepped in when I started to unload—without being asked. Yard work, like cooking, worked best if we predetermined our roles rather than me expecting him to be able to read my nonverbal signals to partner with me. And last but not least, sex and intimacy also offered great partnerships that were essential, fun, and rewarding for both parties. I won't go into detail here; maybe that is another whole book!

Experiment at Home

Partnering with a person with autism takes purposeful and artful planning. The purpose of partnering is to guide a child (or person of any age) with autism to connect and share control. Each of you should elaborate on your joint play and engagement—leading to new and ever-expanding learning, which we will explore more in the next chapter.

Partnering with a beloved teen or adult in your life will take patience, understanding, and trial and error. It will be an exploration of ways and times that work for partnering while discovering other strengths of your loved one when they are not in the space for partnering. Taking walks, making dinner, playing board games, and other goal-oriented activities are often more successful than open-ended activities with teens and adults with autism, for example.

You must be mindful of the other aspects and accommodations offered in part 1 of this book, "Understand," when you enter the partnerships. Consider whether you are in the right headspace to be partnering, for example. Are you going to potentially add to the flood of sensory and emotional overload because you are stressed about a phone call you have to make for work? Or getting dinner on the table for your children? Or visiting your mom in the hospital? Consider the visual and auditory landscape around you. Is it cluttered? Is the TV on? Are you constantly being interrupted? All of these can set you both up for partnering to be frustrating and much less successful than you had hoped.

Some of my clients enjoy setting aside a predictable time each day when they think about and attempt partnering with their loved one. If you are a professional, this may be a few minutes in your classroom or therapy session that you set aside to think about and offer partnership opportunities. Find a time that is typically quieter when your own head is predictably clear. Then engage in a little preplanning. What might you offer where you genuinely need or would enjoy their help? Carrying something up the stairs with you? Moving the couch so you can vacuum? Opening the board game box to prepare to play together?

We engage in partnerships with others every day in both simpler and more complex ways. We learn from others when engaged in these partnerships. The person who opens the door for us on the way into a store is probably more on the compassionate side. The person who does not is either in a hurry or lost in their own thoughts. They're not necessarily attending to the nonverbal needs of others. When we have a conversation, which is a partnership, we learn about the other person's interests, preferences, and knowledge that we may compare and contrast with our own. This will often shift our thinking based on the conversation.

We learn the basics of partnerships very early in our development. If a person misunderstands or does not engage in these partnerships at a very young age, they may then veer onto a different path for learning, one that is more solitary, concrete, and/or routine.

Almost any activity can be turned into partnering practice. The important aspect is that both people in the interaction have essential and dependent roles. Each role must be contingent on the other. The overall job or activity cannot be completed without each person's essential role. Here are some examples of different partnership types:

- One person hands the other person something to manipulate
- Both people move or carry something that is too heavy for just one of them alone

- Each person takes a turn in a game or activity
- You collaborate to open something together
- You cocreate just one drawing, story, or building rather than two separate ones
- One of you holds something that the other manipulates

Through these examples, an individual is given practice in being an active participant in supported partnerships. As mentioned earlier in this chapter, we start simple, with few distractions, before adding complexity. The partnership will need to be basic at first, with opportunities to slowly support the child's success in being a fifty-fifty partner and adding complexity of multiple partners and distractions.

The 50% Rule

Frequently in my work, I am looking for an easy way to remember the practice I am recommending. For partnering, I suggest committing to the 50% Rule. The 50% Rule requires you to rarely do more than 50% of the work in any given partnership with someone.

It is common for individuals with autism to either take full control and do a task themselves, or to turn away, allowing you to do all of the work for them. For example, a child requests a bag of chips be opened for them. They hand it to you and quickly turn away, allowing you to open it and chase them down once you have it open, or allowing you to prepare it by putting it in a bowl for them and on the table where they can eat. This is not a partnership. This is you doing something *for* them.

With the 50% Rule, you only do half of the work. If they do not take their role, the task or action does not happen. Your child or partner hands you an apple to cut, let's say. With the 50% Rule, you now partner with them to cut the apple together rather than doing it completely for them.

Since partnering can and often should also lead to increased independence, as in the examples above, your partner can always take on more than 50%, but you should not. Please consider that you may have an individual who insists on doing all of the work—100%—so that they can control the outcome. This is also not partnering practice. When we engage with our peers, we do not want to fully control the engagement with them, or we will quickly turn people away from us. By offering this 50% Rule within your daily routines together or during your scheduled partnering time, you are providing beautiful practice that will boost confidence and raise awareness of their impact on others. Their actions within your partnership will create moments of realization that their actions matter and will change your interaction in manageable and even enjoyable ways.

One of my clients, a four-year-old, was walking outdoors and picking dandelions seemingly without regard for his mother, who was nearby. He picked each dandelion and made the stems into the shapes of letters. His engagement with his mother was minimal. To keep the sheer number of dandelions picked to a minimum so they could continue on their walk together, she would say, "Last one" from a given yard and move on to the next.

His mother lamented that they had very little connection out in nature—even though it was something they both obviously enjoy immensely.

We have a choice to view this little boy as being focused on creating letters out of dandelion stems and assume he does not want connection, or we can assume he does want connection but is managing the uncertainty of the walk by creating his own organized "job" or "role" for himself. By presuming competence and his drive for connection, we can help him by creating a structure or a partnership that makes sense for him.

When I offered this perspective and recommendation to his mother, she started offering and engaging in partnerships with him on walks. They created chants and songs to match their walking together in an organized rhythm. They sometimes brought paper bags with them to collect the dandelions to bring home to explore together. Each took turns holding the bag for the other to put the dandelions in. Through making partnership opportunities clear, this little boy and his mother were able to enjoy their love of the outdoors and practice social reciprocity. They gained so much by this mother seeing her little boy for his strengths in organization and natural drive for connection.

Build Confidence in Partnering

People with autism spectrum disorders often find partnering intriguing but challenging, exhausting, and confusing. Therefore, they may avoid interactions or control them through negative behaviors. It is important to support people on the spectrum in engaging in and feeling successful in these partnerships, and to guide them in social reciprocity with others for learning, growing, and loving.

There are several ways you can celebrate someone's participation and build confidence. For example, most of us use verbal praise to highlight accomplishments. This may be fine with your child or partner, but sometimes, for those with auditory processing challenges that are frequently seen in autism, verbal praise may not be as well received. In fact, it may feel aversive to some. Consider observing what works for your partner to feel celebrated. Does a touch and smile help them feel loved and valued as they are partnering with you? Or does a single word or phrase like "teamwork" when you are in synch solidify and mark their engagement? Or does a picture or even a video that you can watch back help them see the value in partnering? Experiment with ways to celebrate. You will find what works best for your partner.

Use Partnering Strategically
In typical development, before an infant can regulate their own systems, they rely on their primary caregivers to help them regulate. This is why we often rock babies or interact with them when they are seemingly unhappy. This is called "coregulation" and looks like a partnership. We may use co-regulation throughout our lives when we are less regulated, borrowing someone else's self-regulation to help us calm and feel regulated again.

In autism, that system of soothing and calming through caregivers often seems to be developing without issue, but then it either stops or seems to decline. The child is less and less likely to initiate a back-and-forth engagement with their caregivers even for soothing (for instance, getting a small injury may result in literally trying to wipe off the wound rather than seeking a parent to soothe them).

Partnering is an innate human need to connect and synchronize. A child may no longer seek it out, but they are still needing that coregulation. In autism, the parent, caregiver, or partner may have to be the initiator for the partnership or offer it in times of need, because the child still needs the coregulation. You may just have to offer it in a different manner. While emergency situations may not be ideal for practicing more complex partnering, they can be excellent times to use partnering strategically to calm a person's system so that their thinking can come back online.

When my own son was about six years old, he attended a weekly tumbling class at a local recreation center. One day we walked in through the front doors and could hear a child screaming, though we could not yet see him. The scream was one of pain and fear. There is an interesting difference in quality of the scream and cry of a child with autism. I'm not sure what it is, but I could tell, and apparently my son could too. My son turned to me and said, "Mom, you need to go help, don't you?" I replied "Yes," and quickly got my son in his seated line for his class.

I made my way to the back of the gym to find the boy with his teacher and mother. The boy was about eight years old. He had obviously endured a nose injury. There was blood everywhere as he thrashed about. The teacher and parent were trying desperately to get him to put ice on his nose. He wanted nothing to do with the ice and continued screaming at full volume.

Between screams, I told them I was an autism specialist and asked if they would like my help. They agreed, and I asked for the ice pack. They told me, "He won't put it on." I said I know and asked again for the ice pack. They gave it to me.

Silently I crouched down below the child's eye level to ensure that he knew instinctively that I was not a threat. I put a gentle smile on my face and took a deep breath. I offered the ice pack toward his knee. He swiped it away. Already I had the makings of a partnership: I offered, he swiped away. I offered it again on his other knee while playfully smiling. He swiped it away but in a slightly calmer manner. I then put the ice pack on his foot, then his other foot, and kept this going as his mother and coach cleaned up his face. His mind was on me and our partnering rather than on the pain and sight of blood. He calmed, and after about five minutes allowed me and his mother to put the ice pack on his nose gently.

Good Times and Bad Times for Partnering Practice

While partnering can be used strategically to guide someone from a bad experience, as in the story about the boy with the bloody nose above, there are good and bad times for practicing partnering—especially when you are supporting more complexity and active participation. Difficulty with complex partnering or social reciprocity is one of the core symptoms of autism. It is one of the hardest or most challenging things for someone when it does not come naturally, or they haven't had the extensive practice that comes with typical development.

This means that partnering can be exhausting. It's true that simple partnering can be a way to bring someone's mind out of a bad or scary place, but more complex partnering may require you, as the guiding partner, to be more mindful of when and how you are presenting the practice.

WRONG TOYS OR MATERIALS

A person with autism may have preferred toys or activities. These may be special interests and things they feel confident doing. It is natural for us to think that these would make great activities for partnering, but they often are not.

When practicing partnering, you have to think about the person's attention and if anything may be competing with you and your partnership. If the person is so fixated on aspects of the toy or activity that they cannot shift their attention back and forth to you, then it is not an activity conducive to partnering practice. Instead of taking it personally or thinking you are doing anything wrong, simply change to a new activity and try again. Choose something similar to their special interest to capture curiosity, but try to steer away from activities where the person has set routines with the materials, or you will simply be competing with those routines.

For example, a young child may be so involved with shaving cream play that you think you can drive toy cars though it together. You may find that the child is so over-focused on the sensory experience that they cannot possibly attend to your additions and partnering opportunities. Another person may enjoy building with Magna-Tiles, so you think they would be perfect for partnering. But that person may have such a strong routine set with how they play with the blocks that any slight change brings them significant stress and inability to partner.

WRONG TIMING

We all have times of the day when we have more and less energy. And we all have good and bad days. When you are offering to partner with someone with autism, remember that this may be tough work for them. Be sure to choose times when they are at their best.

At the same time, if you are rushed, often partnering will not work. You need to be able to give the person processing time. Partnering during a rushed morning routine, for example, may not be the best timing for optimal practice. Partnering as part of the bedtime routine may offer great opportunities for some parents who are night owls, while for other parents it may be too challenging to try to partner at the end of the day when they are at their wits' end.

WRONG ENVIRONMENT, OR WRONG FOR NOW

Partnering in a rush or in a situation that is too visually cluttered or auditorily overwhelming is going to make it very challenging for either of you to partner successfully. You can read more about this in chapter 7, "Decluttering the Environment."

Early on, it is essential to choose an environment that is quiet and distraction free while partnering. Some children or adults need this to be *extremely* quiet and distraction free, to the point of needing a room free of anything else besides you and the item(s) that you are using to partner.

Observe the person to determine what allows them to be fully engaged with you and the materials. As the person becomes more and more successful and fluid with partnering in the quieter environments, you can start adding environmental distractors on purpose to support the person's confidence and ability in busier environments. You might consider a rushed or busy environment as a challenge you later offer to a person who becomes adept at partnering in quieter environments.

A teenage girl in my practice had such high levels of anxiety in public settings that she would engage in severe self-injury. She would drop to the ground and hit her head on concrete, bloodying her face and concerning her parents that she may be giving herself brain damage.

Her parents and support workers committed to spending some time simplifying the world around her so she could find her baseline again. Through their calm and measured support in their partnerships with her, she calmed, reduced her self-injury significantly, and learned to trust those around her to partner with her.

Her parents and support workers added minor complexity slowly. After home practice of partnering in quiet environments with increasing complexity in that familiar location, her parents and people supporting her took her into more public places, such as her favorite coffee shop or the local park, as a measured addition of complexity. Once there, they could partner in familiar games and activities. Where she had once crumbled into severe panic with self-injurious behaviors, she is now able to venture out with often excited anticipation.

Zone of Proximal Development

Lev Vygotsky was a Russian psychologist who gave us a way to think about teaching and guiding when a person is at their best. He stated that children learn new skills within their "zone of proximal development." We all learn optimally when things are offered within and just beyond our current level of development. The zones of learning keep moving as the child continues learning; they are not stagnant zones, but ones that move with the child's growth and development.

For example, once a child learns the basics of partnering with you, you can move on to adding some complexity, which you will learn about in the next chapter. Or for a child who is learning math, once they have the basics of addition, you move on to subtraction. If you stayed with addition, the child would be bored, and if you jump to algebra, you would be teaching significantly out of their zone of proximal development.

The concept of zones allows you to consider what the person is capable of right now and what the next step will be. The next step should be something that will challenge them but not put them over the edge into an overwhelmed or stressed state. And please do not forget: it is also wise to consider the other end of that zone, where we might underwhelm the person with autism. We may offer something that is too simple or not challenging enough, so that the person is bored. We slip into this when we do the same thing over and over again with someone with autism, thinking they like sameness. In actuality, they need you and the partnership with you to challenge them within their zone of proximal development. A good thing to keep in mind is that if you are bored, you can assume your partner is as well.

CHAPTER 12

Being Willing to Experiment

Think of it: a disability is usually defined in terms of what is missing.... But autism...is as much about what is abundant as what is missing, an over-expression of the very traits that make our species unique.
—Paul Collins

Sometimes even the best days can take a turn for the worse. The once-sunny days turn dark and full of behavioral storm clouds. We may become fearful and distraught about our child's or partner's behaviors. It is never in the middle of the storm that we can build or even repair. Every storm eventually eases. We must allow the storm to pass before starting the rebuilding process.

Individuals of all ages with autism commonly have regulation needs. Their sensory and emotional systems seem to react differently to stimuli. They require not a different set of tools and techniques for helping them—and you—through the storms, but a more refined set of the same tools and techniques. Everything you see in autism happens in typical development; it is just a matter of extremes and may show up in different ways.

Autistic individuals may be bothered by different things than you might think is reasonable. Accept that it is a real experience for them. Part of embracing neurodiversity is to respect that their sensory and emotional systems may go on overdrive or shut down at different times than yours.

When the Storm Is Brewing

Recognizing the signs that the storm is brewing is the first step to supporting someone with challenging behaviors. And just a reminder: this is all of us. We all have behaviors that challenge ourselves and others. Typically it is not just one thing that sets us off to lose our cool but many small things that build up. We may wake up a little later than we wanted, which causes us to be a little more rushed than usual. Then we find that we are out of coffee. Then we realize we are late to wake up the kids for school. Then we find that the kids have already been up and spilled a bowl full of cereal in their room. With each incident our stress level rises, our body reacts by becoming tense, our heart rate increases, and our breathing becomes quicker and shallower. We know that this is your body starting to prepare to fight, flee, freeze, faint or fawn.

Autistic adult and advocate Jonathan Chase, in his book and public speaking events, shares his experiences of arriving to school. He shares the things that build up for him are often sensory and routine based. He describes his experience of the building stress as the door he usually enters at school is locked and he has to choose another, his sock being slightly folded beneath his foot, and not only not having a sharpened pencil but also not knowing how or when to ask to sharpen that pencil. All of these individual events pile upon one another and create a stress level that can be unbearable. He shares that all of these things also come into his consciousness at the same level. He's not able to filter or prioritize one over the other.

If you can take the time to observe yourself, your child, or your partner for indications of their building stress, you can also be the one to support them to be at their best. Initiating and requesting help is commonly more challenging for those on the spectrum. It may be a great help to create awareness for that person about their personalized responses to what is happening around them so that they can then advocate for themselves.

For very young children, this may look like validation of their emotional or sensory response to something rather than telling them it is okay or "not a big deal." Many parents and professionals worry that validation will reinforce challenging behaviors. Let me reassure you, you can successfully validate and redirect. You can give the child or person words for their experience while giving them tools to move on more successfully next time. Invalidating their emotional or sensory response will only make the individual feel shame about their experience. Validation and then following through are key.

Please consider writing down a few things you notice in your own or partner's body language as the storm is brewing, what currently helps, and what makes things worse.

It is when the storm is brewing that you can experiment with validation, replacement behaviors, and calming strategies. You can stop talking, pause the activity, and offer alternatives. You can call on your own calm, sit down, and create a safe space for your child or partner to join you.

A particular issue that comes up time and time again with autistic individuals is that they are managing so many multiples of sensory and emotional input that they cannot process or sort through them. They are always on high alert, meaning the storm is almost always brewing. The individual seldom ever feels a sense of calm or safety as their baseline. This is common when parents come to me saying, "The behavior comes out of nowhere. They just go from zero to sixty!" Here the goal must be to help that person have time and space to bring their baseline back to a manageable and safe feeling. This may mean very different things for each individual. Some children simply need more information about their daily life and schedule, maybe using photos to share with them what is happening through their day. Other individuals need quiet in their lives if they are noise sensitive. Others need more traditional things, like better sleep or exercise, to get rid of the excess anxiety and nervousness they feel in their bodies.

Taking the time to experiment with activities and choices to calm one's overall system will provide a cushion to weather the regular storms of life.

Weathering the Storm

Even with the best intentions and interventions, we all have moments when we lose our tempers. We all say things we wish we had not. We all yell sometimes. We all get agitated and show it in very different ways. Individuals with autism commonly struggle with verbal language and may use aggression to demonstrate their frustration and overwhelm. This is what I refer to as weathering the storm. The weather is really bad. You are potentially scared of what may happen. If it was not your storm to begin with, it is now. Your own system has also gone into fight, flight, freeze, or faint mode. This is one of the hardest moments of parenting or working with people with regulation needs. You may start having serious doubts about your own ability to guide, to support, and to befriend the person who is having such a hard time in the middle of the storm, but I am about to share some ideas with you of how to weather that storm, staying as safe as possible.

This is your permission to recognize the storm and prioritize safety. It is not a time to do the hard work, lecture, or try to teach. Both you and the autistic person have now gone into a mode that is not conducive to new learning. It is a biologic response to physical threat. The decision-making and verbal regions of your brain have gone offline in order to help you run away, fight, freeze or fawn to keep you as safe as possible. Your job at this point is simply to ensure that everyone is safe, reduce sensory input, and not add to the storm. Take these steps when you witness that storm for yourself or someone else:

- **Ensure safety:** You may need to move items, other children, or yourself to reduce possible injury.
- **Reduce sensory input:** Look around and reduce any sensory offenders you can. That might mean you turn off the radio, turn the lights down, stop talking, and reduce the number of "helpers."
- **Do not add to the storm:** Sit down if possible so that your own body is not seen as an additional threat, go silent, take deep breaths, ground your feet, and calm your own body.

Again, this is permission to let go and just be safe. It is not a time to teach. Simply calm the storm and ride it out. It will pass. It isn't glamorous, and it isn't a place you or the person with autism wants to be, but it will pass. You may have to even give in and give them what they want in the moment just to keep everyone safe. That is okay, especially if you are committed to coming back to the situation that caused the storm—after it has passed.

GETTING OUT OF CRISIS

When an individual is in crisis mode, they are in a hypervigilant, reactive mode. They are not in a curious or even neutral state for learning. They are focused on finding safety and security. If you present yourself as scattered, stressed, or tense, no person will seek you out as a guide for calming, for security, and for soothing.

Individuals with autism are experiencing sensory and auditory input that often sends them into crisis mode. Therefore, our goals with and for individuals with autism must center on being a calm and predictable guide to build trust and move out of crisis mode. It is always okay to take the time to figure out how to best support yourself and soothe your own system so that you can ideally support someone else in your life.

Here are some first steps for you and your family to ensure safety, security, and trust so that learning and guiding can begin again for an individual with autism.

BECOME A PREDICTABLE GUIDE

Individuals with autism often seek structure or routine when their anxiety is high. Many autistic individuals feel overwhelmed by sensory and social challenges. They may turn inward for structure and routine because it feels soothing. The overwhelm, plus their drive for structure, can look like restricted or repetitive behaviors, aggression, bolting, or self-injury. These reactions all aim to stop or reduce the offending input.

While it may seem like a good idea to follow their lead, try to solve issues for them, try to keep the peace, or change your actions to appease them, these actions will probably just add to their flood. They are seeking structure and sameness. If we chase them while trying to find a way to help, we leave them flailing without structured direction. We may fall into chasing individuals with autism down these paths rather than supplying the security they seek.

By following the tenets in this book, you are working to gain the trust of a person with autism to feel safe enough to experiment and learn most effectively.

GO SILENT OR REDUCE WORDS SIGNIFICANTLY

Many adults on the autism spectrum share that they frequently experience sensory overload of auditory and other sensory information. Going silent or significantly reducing your words can ensure regulation quickly.

We tend to talk too much during transitions, for example, which is a commonly stressful time for everyone but especially for those who also experience stress with uncertainty. So instead of trying to fix, change, or soothe with words, consider simply going silent and reducing the flood of auditory processing required for that individual.

CREATE BALANCE FOR YOURSELF

Having a balanced brain yourself is critical for guiding your child to achieve balance and regulation. According to *The Yes Brain* by Dr. Daniel Siegel and Dr. Tina Payne-Bryson, having a balanced brain "means considering our options and making good decisions—being flexible. And it means being able to return quickly to stability after difficult moments and feelings, the basis of equanimity. It means maintaining control of one's mind and emotions and behaviors and handling difficult emotions and circumstances well" (Siegel and Payne-Bryson 2019).

SCHEDULE TIME FOR YOURSELF

Schedule a daily, predictable time for yourself to regroup *away* from autism and your child. Exercise. Read (something not autism related). This is not time to schedule appointments, unless they are for you to spend time with a friend, go for a walk or run, or get a massage. If this means that you need help from others around you, ask. Time for yourself is essential for supporting those around you.

CONNECT WITH ANOTHER CAREGIVER

You will need support from and a connection with someone else who knows your child well. If this person is regularly in the home, decide on a code word or action that you can each use if you are feeling overwhelmed and need a break. Schedule time with this caregiver while your child is occupied so that you can ensure you are on the same page about behaviors, goals, and schedules.

SCHEDULE MEALS

Schedule meals at specific and predictable times. Do not waver. You need to eat. Your child needs to be offered food, even if you or your child are not ready to eat yet. Continue offering food at that predictable time each day.

SCHEDULE INTERNET TIME FOR YOUR FAMILY

Schedule when your internet will be on and off throughout each twenty-four-hour period. If you do not know how to turn your internet on or off, find out. Ask someone to help you. Be honest and post these times for your family. It is not a secret. You are setting clear boundaries and standards you believe are going to help you and your child get the sleep you both need.

Be reasonable and think about your child's age. If they are an older teen, for example, you may need the internet to go off later than for a younger child—or you may need to negotiate the time for mutual agreement.

SCHEDULE TIME TO CONNECT

Schedule at least three times per day that you or someone trusted simply connects with your child, without an agenda. No nagging. No trying to get them to do anything in particular. Just be with your child to observe, respond, and process with your full attention. Each of the three connection times can start as just a quick moment and grow to as much as twenty to thirty minutes. Gauge how much connection your partner can benefit from, and always try to end on a positive note. My goal is usually to leave them wanting more. If you allow the time together to wane and end negatively, there is a good chance they will not be jumping at the opportunity when it's presented in the future.

SCHEDULE TIME FOR SPECIAL INTERESTS

Be sure to include time for special interests in your daily schedule together. This is time when you not only allow but encourage your child's special interests. If you ignore or avoid them, they will often become more obsessive, and the child will feel they have to fight for that time. Having at least some predictable time for the child to explore their special interests will alleviate stress and anxiety about when they may happen.

VISUALLY POST YOUR DAILY SCHEDULE

Both you and your child or partner need to be able to see the schedule of the events. Make your schedule simple, straightforward, and clear. If your child can read, use simple, single words. If your child is not yet reading, use photos or drawings. If you are not sure how to do this, ask for help making it clear and visual for your child. A speech pathologist, autism specialist, or occupational therapist can help with this.

A ten-year-old client in foster care was struggling with basic, everyday tasks like brushing his teeth, getting dressed, and helping out around the home. He needed prompting for every step and was seemingly not wanting to be as independent as most ten-year-olds. The family was amazing and kind, and they wanted so badly to ensure a calm, stable home for him. They brushed his teeth for him, chose his clothes and physically dressed him, and had very few demands for his participation in home chores.

This left him without a structure to settle into, and he continued to struggle when things didn't go as he had planned. His life prior to the placement in foster care had been full of change and uncertainty. His behaviors were to become rigid and controlling of his surroundings.

Slowly we helped him understand the schedule by having it up in his room: when he was to go to school, when he would see his biological family, and when the daily tasks would occur. By having a predictable schedule made visual, he became increasingly calm. With the addition of taking more of the responsibility for his own dressing and even household chores, he began to learn how to share control, feel successful, and even initiate more with peers and adults. It was by alleviating his stress of the unknown that we helped him find a calm baseline so that he could then manage life's stressors more successfully.

COMMUNITY CARDS

Some families find it helpful to plan for community outings and activities by having informational cards with them. There are many of these available from different autism agencies, and you can find them online to print. Many include simple "this is autism" information for onlookers who are curious about autism.

Thank you for your concern. We've got this, but you could help by getting and keeping the environment around us quiet and reducing the number of people. Thank you.

The behaviors that usually gain the most attention are those that are the most dangerous. Children or teens who are dropping to the floor, running into traffic, or physically hurting themselves or others bring the public's attention. The public inquiries are usually well-meaning, and people wish to help, although there are certainly those who feel it is their obligation to rudely tell you how to parent your child without an inkling of understanding. Just stay focused and let go of those comments. Do not take them personally. They do not walk in your or your child's or partner's shoes.

I've included a sample card for you to use here. Consider making your own cards that share what is most helpful for you and your child or partner in those moments of an escalated storm.

After the Storm Has Passed

It is after the storm has passed when most of us breathe a sigh of relief that things seem to be easing up. Sometimes people— autistic or not—feel remorse that they lost their temper and will apologize or try to make up for the challenging situation. It would be very easy, and it even seems respectful, to simply drop it and not discuss the issue again. I suspect that you will not be surprised to hear me say that this might not be the best long-term solution. Instead, try the following steps.

PUT A FLAG IN IT

One of my wise and wonderful clients said that she learned this concept of returning to tough moments and would think of it as putting a flag in the moment. The flag is simply a note to remind you to return to the moment that caused the flare-up of emotions, overwhelm, or challenge for you and for the individual. Avoiding it is not going to help that person learn alternatives. It will only teach them to avoid or repeat their behavior in that situation.

WRITE IT DOWN

Write down exactly what happened. The more objective you can be, the better. Instead of writing "They had a meltdown," try to be more specific. You might write, "They fell to the floor, screamed, and started hitting me." This will help you either to think about each of the behaviors in isolation or to speak with professionals about the behavior you wish to see decrease.

DETERMINE THE WHY

There are professionals available to help you determine why the meltdown happened. Ask your child's or partner's teacher, job coach, case manager, or other professional for help with what is called a Functional Behavior Assessment. Basically, it is a process for you and the team supporting your child or partner to determine why the behavior is happening.

You may already have suspicions, but sometimes those are not correct. It is common that people think children are doing things for attention, for example, when they are bored or escaping a situation that is sensorily overwhelming. If we base our next steps on an incorrect assumption about why the behavior is occurring, we spin our wheels, and the behavior will continue to happen or crop up in different ways. Many educators, therapists, and child development specialists will accurately state that "all behavior is communication." It is our job to figure out what they are trying to say.

PLAN TO PRACTICE REPLACEMENT BEHAVIORS

Figure out replacement behaviors that will serve the same purpose as the reason for the behavior in the first place. If you determine that your child or partner is acting out due to being overwhelmed, you might support them in learning to ask for a break or to politely ask people to be quiet. If your child is hitting because they are bored, you might offer and teach them to choose from activities that are available to them, and then add new or different ones regularly to avoid future boredom.

The key here, though, is to plan for practice when you and your child or partner is at their best. We cannot teach in the middle of the storm. The replacement behaviors must be taught when the situation is not as volatile. Take the time to plan for practice.

Rebuilding to Better Withstand Future Storms

While our primary goal is to weather the storm safely, we also want to ensure the person is ready to be successful and make good decisions in future situations in life. We want to build resiliency through practice and confidence in decision-making. We can offer these through the practice mentioned above, but there are a few other ways to help someone withstand future storms as well.

Everyone needs to feel in control of their own lives through choices. We learn from an early age that our actions impact the world around us. Developmentally, children start to demand their control around two years of age with statements like "Mine!" Later, older children and teens may refuse to do things they used to do willingly. It is not because they forgot how to do them; it is because it may be the only way for them to feel some control or personal agency over their own life.

It's completely normal for all of us, autistic or not, to want this personal agency. This may or may not occur in autism in the same way, however. You may experience a person's drive for control through an increase of behaviors or a retreat into rigid routines. A person may retreat to their room or say no to joining team meetings or family engagements. Knowing what you now know about autism, you can provide clear and specific choices for an autistic individual to feel settled, share control, and feel more confident.

As with everything in this book, it may take some time and practice to undo habits and regain trust in new ways of communicating. By both giving choices and providing clear boundaries, you raise your expectations that that person can thrive within them. By finding a balance between the two that works most ideally for your child or your partner, you are respecting that every person with autism is different from one another. And by involving your child's or partner's team of friends, neighbors, relatives, and professionals to ensure respect and consistency, you are following a recipe for success.

The art of building relationships with anyone, including those with autism, is through mindful experimentation. The person with autism learns to become resilient and take risks by learning to engage in the trial-and-error learning cycle. It is a parallel process for you to learn to experiment with what works for you in relation to the person with autism, while the person with autism learns to experiment with what works for themselves and others.

As the person guiding, we may feel the following:

- Resistance: The individual with autism or we ourselves seem rigid, hypervigilant, or anxious, or are simply in shutdown mode.
- Boredom: You are bored or feel seeming disinterest from your partner, and they are becoming rigid or exhibiting challenging behaviors such as aggression or shutdown.
- Frustration: You or your partner are becoming rigid, hypervigilant, and potentially aggressive.

Move to Fascination

When we feel resistance, boredom, or frustration, shifting our lens to one of fascination will enable us to move to a better place for connection and guiding. Fascination provides us with an opportunity to explore why you or your partner is reacting or responding in that way. If we stay resistant, bored, or frustrated, we may start to place blame on ourselves or others. We may stay stuck in a loop of that feeling instead figuring out a way out.

Taking a look at how much uncertainty we are offering that is causing either resistance, boredom, or frustration can provide some insight. It is quite common for people with autism to simply need modifications to be successful within interactions. These modifications include a reduction of uncertainty, which means making things a bit more structured or offering a bit more choice or control. By being willing to experiment, we can find the sweet spot of shared control and connection that deepens relationships.

Being willing to experiment requires you to be in the moment—in a state of observation and wonder. Experimenting requires you, as the friend or guide, to be resilient and strong so that you can share your calm and confidence. If you are frequently agitated or frustrated, you will not be calming your own system enough to observe what is happening for you and your partner. This is required for successfully determining the why behind the behaviors and then what you can do to help alleviate them. If it is the case that you are frequently agitated, please take time to go back to the section on self-care in chapter 3. It will be the greatest gift you can give to your child, client, friend, or partner.

Being willing to experiment also requires you to be in touch with your own and the other person's regulation. The first step needs to be reading the autistic individual's various states from calm to agitation. Sometimes it can feel as if the escalation and aggression come out of nowhere, but this commonly means you or the individual with autism is in a hypervigilant state much of the time and may need overall support for calming. You will need to know the signs that they exhibit when they are feeling over- or underwhelmed to be able to experiment with the edges of those—guiding your child or partner to an integrated and healthy state of being.

Plot Twists

Experimenting with the edges of one's comfort zone involves minor risk-taking. Risk-taking usually comes naturally to children and adults who are considered neurotypical. In fact, as parents and partners of individuals who are considered neurotypical, our role is often one of guiding them to remain within realms of safety. When teens want to do things outside of our comfort zone, for example, our role is to remind them to stay safe or to limit their ability to put themselves in danger.

In autism, the drive for risky behavior is often not the case and is in fact the opposite. They find routine and predictability soothing, grounding, and comfortable. They have experienced frequent failure when they have tried to stretch outside of their comfort zones, and so they stay. We are often the ones who need to guide them to take risks and to learn that taking small risks can teach them about themselves, build confidence, and even build connections with others.

In autism, we must assume that they have been pushed past their comfort zones at some point in their development. They either pushed themselves, or someone pushed them past where they could handle it and be resilient. They have landed in a state of almost constant hypervigilance or have settled into a comfort zone that is narrow and lonely. We have the opportunity to guide someone with autism to approach or return to that edge of safety to experiment in ways that both stretch their comfort zone and build resiliency.

One clever dad I worked with called this offering "plot twists": offering tiny moments within your interaction where instead of staying in the straight and static, you veer a little off the path, just enough for a moment of uncertainty that soon gets resolved.

An example of this might be a father and son making a bed together. They go to the closet to retrieve the sheets together, then they start pulling the bottom sheet onto the bed in a nice partnership. Each is tugging on one corner together. The straight and static path would be do it like you always do it: count "one, two, three" as you tug together and pull that corner over the mattress. But today you decide to offer a plot twist. Instead of counting "one, two, three" like you always do, you count "one, two, four!" and pull it over. Or you slow down your counting, or you count in Spanish, or another language you know or make up. You might also start to pull using your 50% Rule from chapter 11, but then you purposely lose your grip and fall onto the bed on the count of "two."

Allow the plot twist to sink in. Do not solve it right away or apologize. Simply allow it to sink in—and allow for your partner to seek your engagement. When they do, this is a moment of their initiating joint attention, which harkens back to chapter 1. It is in these small playful moments that you can bring to life your practice with social reciprocity, which will provide your partner with the foundation for lifelong success in relationships with others. Allowing your partner to feel a moment of uncertainty that is not only manageable but intriguing sets the stage for learning and engagement in our ever-changing, sometimes chaotic lives with each other.

For many of us, feelings of uncertainty can be positive and filled with joyous anticipation rather than fear and resistance. We anticipate someone coming home from a long time away. We anticipate cookies being done, fresh from the oven. We anticipate going somewhere we have been looking forward to visiting. One of my deepest moments of sadness comes when I watch children with autism experience a moment of potential joyful anticipation, but instead they try to control it, responding with fear and trepidation.

We all experience fear of the unknown, and that out-of-control feeling is unbearable at times. As I write this book, we're in the middle of the 2020–2021 COVID-19 pandemic. We are all experiencing fear of the unknown. We do not know what the world will be like in a month, let alone by the time this book is published. We are hunkering down in our homes to stay safe and do what we can to stave off the worst-case scenarios. Now imagine that your daily life felt that uncertain, even when there is no pandemic. What if socializing in everyday life felt like socializing in the middle of a pandemic? We feel anxious about even passing others by on the street and going to restaurants, making us question our safety. This is how many people with autism feel about the uncertainty that typical socializing brings. Therefore, the person either goes into hypervigilant mode—seeing and perceiving danger and unpredictability in most situations—or completely shuts down to avoid trouble, uncertainty, and change. It is not surprising that people with autism commonly experience diagnosable anxiety along with their autism.

If you are parent, friend, or professional, you may at times find yourself in what is known as a "reactive mode" with your partner on the autism spectrum. You may be triggered by their behavior rather than being able to provide a learning moment or plot twist. You are most likely trying to stop negative behaviors that are occurring in front of you. Understandably, when you are in reactive mode, you are not fully considering the long-term or relationship needs of the person. A person who repeats themselves or is echolalic may feel annoying to you, and you just want them to stop. The person who becomes aggressive when his device or favorite item is taken away will be seen as manipulative.

Being reactive often comes from a place of fear and frustration. We may fear that we are giving in if we choose to soothe someone, or we may fear losing control of someone when they are being stuck, rigid, or aggressive. Sometimes we are fearful for our own safety due to past aggressions. All of these can cause us to be in reactive mode rather than being able to respond to our partners with the relationship in mind.

Check Your Bias

Teachers and professionals who are unfamiliar with autism until they have a child in their classrooms or caseloads may feel underqualified in the field of autism and fearful that they may do or say the wrong thing. They may try to avoid engaging the child altogether, allowing others who are more experienced to engage them in separate classrooms or within their classrooms. They may also hold biases about children with autism being manipulative or overly sensitive.

Your own personal and inherent biases must be addressed before you walk in the door to engage with the children you serve; otherwise, your reactions may miss the mark completely in serving the children you wish to support. You will not be listening and experimenting in the zone that is most appropriate to spark curiosity and experimentation with the particular child you wish to serve.

In considering inherent biases we hold, note that Black children with autism are considerably more likely than white children with autism to be expelled, excluded, segregated, and seen as behaviorally problematic versus overwhelmed. This statistic shows the extreme potential for our inherent bias in each of us, and it must be seen, addressed, and rectified.

As we learned in earlier chapters, if we are working from a place of fear, we will not be able to be the calm and collected self we wish to be for our autistic partner. Fear is such a visceral, body-felt experience. It keeps us safe from immediate danger. It helps us avoid situations that could put us in real, physical danger. Our brains shut down the areas reserved for experimenting, long-term thinking, and planning. Our bodies react by shutting down our digestion temporarily and activating hormones in our systems so we can fight or flee. These are all very helpful reactions of our bodies and brains if we are running from a lion or fighting off an attacker. We do not need these reactions when building relationships with one another. We need to be able to make thoughtful choices and responses.

In fact, when we are in this reactive mode, we are biologically unable to think clearly to make the choices we would when our systems are in more relaxed states. When you have cortisol coursing through your veins, you are biologically unable to be curious or inquisitive. You are simply in a hypervigilant, safety-seeking mode. By recognizing your own fear reaction and then taking steps to understand and alleviate that fear, you afford yourself the opportunity for fascination and wonder. Being in a state of fascination and wonder about another human being opens the door to relationship building and true connection, whether you are a parent, teacher, friend, loved one, or professional.

Moving from fear, boredom, and frustration to fascination opens up the possibility of understanding the why behind behaviors that challenge you. You can wonder and discover that a person who echoes you or is repetitive is simply trying to connect with you, but they are stuck in their own reactive mode. You discover ways to reduce their reactive mode in order to gain new perspectives on their learning and processing. You learn how to provide opportunities for new risks into the realm of uncertainty without fear, rigidity, or shutdown.

Your Own Fear

Recognizing your own fear of upsetting the person or doing something wrong must be considered. If you are always trying to keep the peace and not rock the boat, then you may be reinforcing the behavior, reinforcing the fear of uncertainty, lowering expectations for that person, or avoiding challenges that may be key learnings for the person you are supporting or who you love. We must be cognizant of our own fears that may be holding us and our children or partners back from learning and engaging.

A colleague and I often confer with each other about seemingly complicated individuals with autism and their families. The individual may be especially aggressive or especially withdrawn. The family may seem more complex due to myriad reasons. We always ground one another and share that "this is autism." We remind each other that the individual is either overwhelmed, under-whelmed, or simply needs more information.

People with autism are not commonly malicious or prone to manipulate others. They experience the world differently. And through understanding, we can reduce fear and support the person more fully—not only respecting but celebrating their different ways of considering the world around them.

Going Over the Edge

You will make mistakes when experimenting with your partner. You will upset the person you are guiding. Take those opportunities to understand what their behavior is communicating to you, then make adjustments accordingly. Allow yourself to be fascinated and curious enough to figure things out. Find the window of tolerance or that river of well-being. Bump up against the edges of that comfort zone. Stretch that comfort zone slowly, deliberately, and creatively—but do not shy away from experimenting.

When offering new opportunities to stretch and build resiliency, your child or partner may say no, which is a very common habit for those on the spectrum to protect themselves. Instead of taking this refusal personally, make the conscious choice to let go and be curious. Turn that frustration into fascination.

Often the issue between you is not anyone's fault, but rather a misunderstanding or a bad timing issue. Maybe you made a statement that was taken literally, and you did not realize it until later. Maybe you attempted to engage with them when it seemed they were available, but it turned out they had something else on their mind. Either way, placing blame or staying frustrated will never work. I promise. Choosing to take a step back, calm yourself, and assess differences in processing might be just what is most needed for connection and understanding between you.

Autistic Fear

People with autism are often working from a place of fear of failure. They may need to feel safe before they can engage in new learning and experimenting. No one can be fascinated if they are experiencing fear; our brains simply do not work that way. When experiencing fear, our brains shut down the areas for decision-making based on contemplation and move our energy and thinking to the areas that can spring to action quickly or shut down if necessary.

The fear that I witness with those on the spectrum can also be seen as a well-worn habit as someone grows into teen- and adulthood. It may be so ingrained that they have now accepted their avoidance of uncertainty to be a personality trait. Adults on the spectrum may have learned that they dislike change, that they like routine, or that they simply are not social beings. They may say no to anything new and uncertain out of habit or acceptance of who they are at their core. While this may be true, long ago in their development, it may have been a fear response. Their neurological and sensory systems were put into overdrive to maintain safety so that they grew and developed in that hypervigilant space—avoiding change and social uncertainty.

Autistic individuals are people first. They have the same drives for love, connection, and belonging as everyone else. It would be a shame if we simply accepted that one was not capable of growth. We know from neuroscience and behavioral research that we are capable of learning and growing at any age.

I ask you to consider and specifically address the fear of failure. I have not met even one adult on the spectrum who did not identify with a fear of failure at almost every turn of life. They learn to not even try due to the prediction of failure. This fear of failure can paralyze someone into inaction. If you have a child, teen, or adult with whom you are partnering, you may have some habits to wade through that have created depression, anxiety, and shutdown due to this fear of failure. This does not mean that the core desires for love, connection, and belonging have gone away. It means they have "accepted their fate" and do not think what they want matters anymore.

Part III

Are You Seeing Autism?

By applying the information you glean in this book, you are one step closer to seeing autism. And by seeing autism, you will be better equipped to connect with someone on the spectrum. Seeing them may be the only intervention that is necessary.

What stood out to you in this section?
What would you like to remember?

Getting Curious

Using Mindful Communication

Creating Partnerships

Being Willing to Experiment

Holding on to Hope

We contain the shapes of trees and the movement of rivers and stars within us.
—Patrick Jasper Lee

I f your child or partner has autism, it does not mean their learning or engagement has ceased. Despite what you may have been told, it does not mean you need a whole different set of tools or techniques for guiding them. It does mean that their development is delayed in certain areas and not in others. It does mean you will need to take better care of yourself so you can be the best parent, friend, or partner possible. It does mean that you may need to get comfortable with long pauses and silence to provide them time to respond. In a nutshell, you will need to hone your people skills.

The funny thing about my work is that everything in this book can apply to anyone, but these techniques are absolutely imperative for someone on the autism spectrum. We all need quieter environments to think at our best. We all must attend to what aggravates our nervous systems, and we all feel better when we know what our role is in given social situations. You are called to use what you have learned in this book more strategically and mindfully, but all are tools we can use with each other, autism or not, to connect more fully.

Is It Ever Too Late?

I am frequently asked, "Is it too late? Can they still learn?" I do believe that the earlier we can support children with autism, the better it is for long-term success in relationships, school, and overall quality of life. The older a person gets, the more routines have been established and habits have become ingrained.

That said, I also strongly believe and have seen that when support is provided at any age, it can be life changing. I have worked with more clients than I can count and know that people can learn and grow at any age. It may take more deliberate practice and more dedication from those around that person, but the time and attention will pay off. When a person feels seen, they blossom.

While I am an early interventionist by training, I now work with teens and adults much more often than I used to. It is usually their parents who bring teens in when they are worried about their future independence. And adults commonly self-refer to my services to explore and better understand their own processing so they can have more personal agency over their lives and futures. The motivation to try out new things may have layers of habits and feelings of incompetency covering it up, but once they feel safe enough to share, they fly.

Set Your Sights on the Future

To begin with the end in mind means to start with a clear understanding of your destination. It means to know where you are going so that you better understand where you are now and so that the steps you take are always in the right direction.
—Stephen R. Covey

I know this may seem trite, but there's a reason Stephen R. Covey made a fortune. He guided us to think about the end result we are aiming for and then to set our goals for today accordingly. Most of my clients come to me in a state of crisis, and they may have been in this state for a while. Major behaviors are getting in the way of living safely together, or depression has set in, leaving them housebound, for example. Still others may be upset that their child is not being integrated or is being integrated but is overwhelmed. Living a life of putting out fires is no way to live. It will not get you to the place where you wish to be or wish your child, partner, or friend to be.

I always start with new clients by making recommendations for how to recognize that they are in crisis and then how to get out of said crisis first. You might refer to chapter 12 for some tips on getting out of crisis. I recently simplified it for a client by telling them to do the following:

- Get low
- Get quiet
- Get predictable

These three simple things can help someone with autism feel less threatened and safer. You may have to embrace these for a week—or two or three—before you see the autistic person relax and be ready to connect.

Once you start to emerge from crisis, or if you are already there, I urge you to assess your current goals for the individual with autism. Are you trying to get them to be compliant? Are you trying to get them to do well academically? Are you teaching them scripts for social skills groups so they can use those scripts with peers? These are all very short-sighted goals. They are goals to fix the person or make someone fit in rather than think for themselves for the long run.

Consider thinking bigger. I know you may be concerned about trying to be "realistic," but people rise to our expectations. If we set our sights low, they will rise to meet those low expectations. And if you set your sights too high, you can always make adjustments along the way. So allow yourself to dream again. Allow yourself to imagine that the child in your care or the adult you love can and will be capable of successful relationships. Imagine a year from now—imagine them having a close friend who they can hang out with doing something they both love. Instead of working on compliance, imagine introducing them to new experiences in small, manageable ways to work toward those goals. Think developmentally so you know you are supporting the foundations. If you want the person to have friends and colleagues to engage with socially, engage with them socially now using the partnerships offered in this book.

Not everyone is going to understand the small steps you are taking toward these long-term goals. You will have daily successes that only some people in your life will understand, but find those people and celebrate those successes. Every step and every moment of connection matters. As you may remember from chapter 1, our brains are never set in stone.

There is a saying in the neuroscience communities: "What fires together, wires together." In other words, if you practice something enough, it will become a habit or a new way of processing. The field of interpersonal neurobiology was established by clinical professor of psychiatry at the UCLA School of Medicine, Dr. Daniel Siegel. This field of study combines our understanding of our brains and bodies, as well as the interactions we have with others. It is the interactions within ourselves and with others that guide how we learn and grow into healthy, satisfied adults or into unhealthy, less satisfied adults. We have come to understand that our brains are not set in stone at any age. The information we receive from our bodies, each other, and our environments affects and changes the way we interpret the world. At any age, we can learn new things, and our brains can literally change how we process information. We adapt to our surroundings and expand our repertoire of living every minute of every day. By engaging in manageable amounts of change, we not only tolerate but look forward to and anticipate new learnings.

I have been meeting with Joanne and her husband for several years now, off and on. Initially we met routinely to help them ensure their understanding of what and how to target the basics of engagement as the cornerstone of all interventions. Joanne is in her thirties, and they have three children. Two of their children have autism, and one does not. You could say that her day is busy, to put it lightly.

One January day, she joined our online call with her usual sweet smile and kind greetings, but I could see the distractedness behind her eyes. She was fidgety, and her facial expressions were lax. Her gaze shifted from side to side. She seemed to avoid looking directly at me. She looked exhausted and wired at the same time. She started out by stating that her husband needed to take a call for work that he had been waiting on all day, so he would not be joining us. She also shared something like, "We haven't done anything." They had cancelled our last session, so I knew they were struggling with adding things to their plate.

I took the share as her feeling like she had to admit to me that she felt like a failure and that we may have to discontinue services for a while. We have done this in the past when they have needed breaks, but also when they have felt things were in a good state—allowing things to marinate a bit.

Today I could tell she was low and not feeling successful. She started talking about how her sensory issues were getting in the way of parenting, how everything felt overwhelming, and how sometimes she just needed to hide under the covers and rest. She would let the children watch shows or grab easy food just so she could regroup. While we all have those days, these were coming frequently and unrelentingly for Joanne. She was trying to manage from a neurotypical perspective—trying to fix what ailed her to try to be at her best.

She had been there before. I had never asked her directly about her own relationship with autism processing. I always allow adults, especially parents, to listen and hear what I have to say and share or ask questions when they are ready. With Joanne, it was the same. She had many times over the years alluded to the fact that she processes differently, gets overwhelmed with sensory input, and needs time for resets.

On this day, I asked her if she'd ever heard about "autistic burnout." I offered her a simple description; her face lightened and her eyes brightened. She started gazing directly at me through the screen. I knew it was hitting home. She was feeling heard and seen. I went on to share the spoon theory and token theory described by those with lupus and autism, respectfully. I shared with Joanne that she might start each day with a certain number of spoons and that she had to choose where she would spend those spoons. She may have to spend three spoons to take a shower or make a meal—leaving her to make decisions about how she would chat with her children's teachers or her own family. She nodded and looked directly at me. As our conversation ebbed and flowed into other topics, she started implementing the analogy fluidly as "using her spoons."

As the conversation progressed (mind you, this is a thirty-minute call), she shared that she had "only been able to play" with her eldest son, about whom she and her husband had been most concerned. She shared that he had "not made any progress in his communication" with others, which had been their latest push in their family efforts. I reminded her that my last assignment for them had been to reconnect with him through play and daily life—to reopen the feedback system between them and reengage him nonverbally so that speech could come more naturally. I celebrated that both Joanne and her husband had taken this assignment and run with it. Just then, her smile returned. She wanted to tell me about an exciting moment during one of their tickle-fest play sessions. Apparently they had been relaxing and playing for a few minutes when he turned, looked at her, and said, "Nana." She asked, "Do you want a banana?" He said "no," then repeated, "Nana." Again, she was confused and tried to offer him a banana. He again refused. He paused and thought for a moment (one of my favorite moments of thinking rather than reacting to the frustration) and then said his words a little more clearly: "Nigh-nigh." Now, apparently it was ten o'clock in the morning, so Joanne was again confused. So she said, "You want night-night?" He brightened and gazed at her with anticipation. She realized that every night, she has a routine of playfully saying "night-night!" while opening and closing the door before a full silly cuddle-fest together. He was requesting that game!

I celebrated with her, as the moment was full of the wonderful back-and-forth that we had been targeting as the foundation of engagement. We were overjoyed together that he persisted to help her understand and that he knew he could trust her to figure out what he had on his mind through their connection. And I carefully and deliberately brought her back to her own statement that she felt he had not made any progress in his communication. She lit up and connected the dots. She became animated and full of relief by realizing and verbalizing that not only were she and her husband not failures, but that through playing and seeing their son, they were doing exactly what he needed. And he was making significant progress. She was so excited to share the reframe and celebration with her husband, breathing new energy into their playtime with their sons.

Celebrate Neurodiversity
The world needs all kinds of minds.

—Dr. Temple Grandin

When I first considered writing a book, I thought about sharing all the wonderful things I think that people with autism are teaching us as a society. Maybe that book will come in the future, but for now, I leave it for you to ponder. So many of us strive to live in the moment, noticing the little things, the details. We strive to say what we mean and to remember facts and figures as we get older. Most people with autism do all of these things naturally. They may get so caught up in a given book, game, or task that they forget what time it is. They commonly state bluntly what they need or want, or what is on their mind, without socially nuanced jargon. While people with autism can lie, it is usually out of fear or preservation rather than manipulation.

Autistic people have fabulous ideas and amazing and wicked senses of humor at times. We need to raise our expectations for their contributions to the world and in the smaller day-to-day moments.

My favorite days of the week are those when I have individual sessions with clients with autism. I adore parents and professionals, but when I get to speak directly with someone with autism, I feel like I witness a deeper sense of living. I feel incredibly grateful.

One client tells me through his letterboard about his desire to work, his frustration with his own repetitive behaviors, and his love for his family. Another client shares incredible introspection about his sensory and emotional experiences, his exploration of possibly being an empath but being stuck due to the incredible overwhelm of the news blasting stories about the latest atrocities in the world. Another shares with me his deep appreciation for those fighting on the front lines for social justice, including the Black Lives Matter movement, yet he still feels confusion over a social media post from a long-lost friend.

Xavier DeGroat became the first autistic intern in the White House. He strove to break barriers there to help the institution and the nation better understand autism. And according to an *Autism Parenting Magazine* article, "Xavier also put together a draft of ideas for new legislation in Congress to help improve Homeland Security and FBI relations with those on the autism spectrum. His ideas included better provision of special services for people with autism at airports under Transportation Security Administration (TSA), and throughout all federal sites"(Elfer 2021).

You may have heard of Greta Thunberg, environmental activist and autistic, who has taken it upon herself to start and continue her strike for climate change. She became *Time* magazine's Person of the Year in 2019. She is quoted in *Time* as stating, "'We can't just continue living as if there was no tomorrow, because there is a tomorrow,' she says, tugging on the sleeve of her blue sweatshirt. 'That is all we are saying'" (Alter, Hayes, and Worland 2019). In 2018, she began a school strike in her home country of Sweden that motivated students across the globe to pay attention to and rally for the protection of our precious environment.

If you haven't checked out the movie *Wretches and Jabberers* yet, I highly recommend you do. It is a movie about two men who are both autistic and communicate with assistive devices to speak for them. Larry Bissonnette is an artist and disability rights activist; Tracy Thresher is an advocate for people with disabilities. The movie is a documentary of their travels across the world meeting others who are also autistic and speak through devices and sharing their stories. The two men are truly inspirations for so many of us to break out of our current bubbles where we may feel stuck. The mission as stated on their website is as follows: "Through advocacy and education, we seek to change attitudes about disability and to support the rights of people who are not able to speak. Our goal is for all individuals to be able to live and learn in their own schools and communities, and have lifelong access to a meaningful way to communicate."

And there are countless others who don't make the news but touch our souls. They are the ones who dance like no one is watching—inspiring others around them to dance too. They are the ones who are quiet and contemplative, calling us to notice the snow falling, the rain collecting on a leaf, or the sound and the feel of the water flowing out of the faucet.

Every individual with autism deserves the right to social connection. I am a strong advocate for full inclusion in school environments, especially when children are young and all children are learning how to get along with one another. Children with special needs should not have to earn the right to enter their neighborhood or community school. Please consider the rights of all humans to engage with proper accommodations. We all want connection and love. We all deserve the sense of belonging.

Again, I thank you for being here and bringing this new depth of understanding to someone you know with autism. Allow yourself to be fascinated. Allow yourself to slow down and enjoy the smaller moments of living. Allow yourself the gift of friendship or companionship with someone with autism. Trust the path you are on. Keep your gaze ahead, steady, and purposeful. Take the time to smell the roses. You will not be sorry. You will be the lucky one.

Appendix 1:

Self-Care Ideas

One of the many fun parts of my work is helping people think of ways to integrate the information I offer them. We can sometimes think something's a good idea but then get stuck in how to implement it! So here are some lists I have created to help get your own creativity flowing. This is *not* an exhaustive list—it's only just the start. Get curious. Get creative. Experiment.

Self-Care Ideas

- ◊ Read a book.
- ◊ Take a walk.
- ◊ Call a friend.
- ◊ Meditate.
- ◊ Write in a journal.
- ◊ Sit down for a cup of tea or coffee.
- ◊ Write a letter or a card to someone.
- ◊ Make cookies.
- ◊ Sneak in a nap.

◊ Buy yourself flowers.

◊ Color.

◊ Listen to music.

◊ Join and go to the gym.

◊ Attend a class where someone will notice if you don't attend.

◊ Commit to exercise just ten minutes per day.

Ways to Center Yourself in the Moment

◊ Take five deep breaths, holding your breath for a moment at each inhale and each exhale.

◊ Sit down with your arms and hands relaxed.

◊ Ground your feet, place your feet at least shoulder distance apart, and bend your knees slightly.

◊ Scan the environment for safety—look for exits or things that could become dangerous.

◊ Go silent. Stop talking.

◊ Count to ten slowly and silently.

◊ Stretch.

◊ Relax your shoulders.

Couple Care Ideas

◊ Go to a movie or hide away for one at home.

◊ Commit to a weekly "date" for lunch, coffee, or a walk together.

◊ Check out the Gottman Marriage Minute e-newsletter, which is full of ideas for dates and communication.

◇ Hug every day.

◇ Kiss every day as your welcome-home or goodnight routine.

◇ Allow each other to vent without solving.

◇ Give each other scheduled "time off" each week from parenting while the other parent is "on."

◇ Start the day with a hug and/or kiss, and decide on just one (not twenty) mini goal for the day.

Appendix 2:

Visual Supports

As you may recall, I am not going to try to sell you on any particular type of visual support. I want you to try to provide a visually clear environment. That may look differently for each person. Here are some ideas for you to consider, but it is certainly not an exhaustive list.

Ideas for Visuals

◇ Use your body to indicate your intentions (standing up if you want to go somewhere, sitting down if you wish for your child or partner to sit).
◇ Cover things that are off-limits with blankets or other materials.
◇ Use a simple stop sign or the universal red circle with a line through it to indicate things that are off-limits.
◇ Provide mini scripts for engaging with others—anything from greetings to telephone conversations.

◊ Cocreate Social Stories (see page 112) to help someone understand the nuances of social interactions that may feel confusing or overwhelming.

◊ Make your conversation come to life in drawings and/ or written words using a dedicated network.

◊ Cocreate mini schedules for routine things, like their morning or evening routine, and have them post it where they want it to support their understanding and ownership.

◊ Check things off a to-do list for chores, homework, or even steps for preparing a meal.

◊ Use the power of video to document, model, and show progress.

◊ Use a whiteboard for explaining concepts or working through challenges.

◊ Use a mini whiteboard to draw or write what must happen first before the next thing. Label it "1st → then" or use numbers "1 → 2" to ensure clarity.

Appendix 3:

Sensory Supports

M ost autistic people experience sensory information in a different way than neurotypicals. Sometimes offering sensory information throughout the day or when you are asking someone to partner can really help them feel more organized. Here are some ideas for you to try out yourself or with someone you wish to support.

Deep-Pressure Activities

◇ Giving hand, foot, or arm massages
◇ Snuggling under pillows with someone applying pressure as requested by receiver
◇ Snuggling in blankets, pillows, and bedding
◇ Touching or exploring sandpaper or bubble wrap
◇ Finger painting
◇ Swimming or bathing
◇ Kneading dough
◇ Playing with Silly Putty

◇ Playing with Gak
◇ Exploring with shaving cream and then adding objects for further exploration
◇ Making sandcastles or mud pies

Proprioceptive Activities

◇ Stretching
◇ Pushing something heavy
◇ Squeezing something like a rubber ball
◇ Running
◇ Jumping
◇ Lifting
◇ Carrying
◇ Pulling
◇ Chewing
◇ Doing household chores like carrying trash, laundry, vacuuming, or sweeping
◇ Raking leaves
◇ Playing tug-of-war
◇ Wheelbarrow walking
◇ Hitting pillows, balls, or balloons
◇ Climbing
◇ Crawling
◇ Wrestling
◇ Crashing and falling onto the bed or into beanbags or pillows
◇ Using weighted blankets

Vestibular Activities

◊ Jumping on a bed or trampoline
◊ Swinging
◊ Spinning
◊ Riding in a wagon, car, or merry-go-round
◊ Rolling down a grassy hill
◊ Sitting in a rocking chair
◊ Sitting on a therapy/yoga ball

More Sensory Ideas

◊ Supply a bin full of fidgets like Rubik's Cubes, squishy toys, fidget spinners, and Koosh balls.

◊ Offer jobs that involve the person's whole body (such as helping you move a heavy table before sitting down to play a game or focus on an activity).

◊ Put on soothing music to change the mood of the room and environment in preparation or during your interaction, or allow someone to listen to something seemingly distracting while you are interacting with them or they are needing to focus on a task.

◊ Provide gum or other chewy options while interacting or in preparation. For a child or person who bites, you might offer a "bite box" several times throughout the day to decrease that person's need to bite when frustrated, overwhelmed, or simply seeking oral motor stimulation.

Appendix 4:

Processing Time Supports

Everyone has different needs regarding their personal processing time. I cannot say when and exactly how long to give every person of every age. We all, autistic or not, need our processing time respected for us to be at our best. Here are some common situations where you'll need to give someone extra processing time:

When to Give Someone Processing Time

- ◇ They are distraught, and you want them to know you are there for them.
- ◇ They are overwhelmed, and you are there when they are ready to help them make sense of it.
- ◇ You want to tell them you love them.
- ◇ You want to tell them it is time for dinner.
- ◇ They come to you asking the same question they have

asked many times before, and often they already know the answer.

◇   They come to you with a challenging behavior, and you give them the opportunity to work through it to then approach you in a better way.

◇   You are teaching something.

◇   You are sharing something with them.

◇   They wish to share something with you.

◇   They wish to teach you something.

Steps to Give Processing Time

1.   Check in with yourself.
2.   Check your expectations.
3.   Offer a bid to connect.
4.   Wait expectantly.
5.   Count to sixty silently.
6.   Lather, rinse, repeat.

Appendix 5:

Decluttering

Decluttering an environment of extraneous visual and auditory information can be a relief for so many on the spectrum. You might find it beneficial for your own peace of mind as well. It can help organize one's thoughts to have one's surroundings more organized.

Ways to Declutter

◇ If you are sitting at a table or on the floor together, remove all other visually distracting items except what you are choosing for your engagement.
◇ Only have essentials up on the walls of your classroom, clinic space, or room.
◇ Get out into nature regularly to rejuvenate the natural visual senses sans the commercialized, over-stimulating visual landscape we experience every day.
◇ When playing a game together, such as cards, have a visual container for the discarded cards or game elements.

◇ Have a visual location for things to "wait" when they are not allowed in the classroom, at the dinner table, or in the car.

◇ Define spaces for play and other activities at home rather than having them all available randomly (for instance, have a defined reading nook with a special chair, blanket, or rug for sitting, or set up a tent or blanket fort for listening to music).

◇ Organize and label drawers of clothes from top to bottom in order so that the person might get dressed.

◇ Keep things in predictable places in the kitchen to avoid additional overwhelm for the autistic cook.

Appendix 6:

Time for Partner Practice

There are so many opportunities for social engagement practice right in your own home and community. Here are a few ideas of things you can do together that will give you or someone you love with autism great practice with partnering.

Lifestyle Times for Practicing Partnering/
Social Reciprocity

Family Night
- ◊ Dancing
- ◊ Playing charades
- ◊ Making forts
- ◊ Game night
- ◊ Playing hide-and-seek

Housecleaning
◇ Vacuuming
◇ Sweeping
◇ Washing a table
◇ Washing the floor
◇ Dusting
◇ Emptying the dishwasher

Meal Preparation
◇ Opening containers
◇ Stirring ingredients
◇ Pouring liquids (juice, ingredients, etc.) into a container
◇ Washing vegetables
◇ Opening the refrigerator

Mealtime
◇ Setting the table
◇ Eating
◇ Serving food onto plates
◇ Cleaning up after the meal
◇ Clearing the table
◇ Washing dishes
◇ Putting dishes in the dishwasher
◇ Wiping down the table

Taking a Walk
◇ Walking
◇ Skipping, jumping, or walking silly
◇ Picking up mementos like leaves or rocks
◇ Pushing and pulling a wagon

◇ Cleaning up after play
◇ Putting toys in containers
◇ Opening containers
◇ Carrying things together to another room

Reading a Book
◇ Choosing a book
◇ Opening the book
◇ Turning pages

Watching Video
◇ Choosing a video
◇ Taking it out of its container
◇ Pulling a beanbag, blanket, or pillow over while watching

Grocery Shopping
◇ Writing a list together
◇ Taking things off the shelf and putting them in the cart or on the conveyor belt
◇ Singing together a chant about anything

Bathing
◇ Getting undressed
◇ Getting a towel
◇ Turning the water on
◇ Putting toys in the tub
◇ Washing their body
◇ Letting the water out
◇ Getting out

Brushing Teeth
◇ Brushing your teeth at the same time
◇ Putting water on the toothbrush
◇ Putting toothpaste on the toothbrush

Dressing
◇ Opening a drawer
◇ Closing the drawer
◇ Choosing clothes
◇ Putting on a shirt, pants, and socks
◇ Putting on shoes

More Mealtime Ideas

◇ Plan meals together.
◇ Shop together.
◇ Cook together.
◇ Taste, smell, and share moments in the kitchen together (even if they're not cooking, invite others in).
◇ Set the table together.
◇ Set something visual in the middle of the table that is a conversation piece.
◇ Pass something special from person to person as it is their turn to share.
◇ Sit in regular places—then change them regularly as well (start with small changes if necessary).
◇ Light a candle and take turns who speaks and what is said during lighting.
◇ Toast to something each night.

◇ State something you are thankful or grateful for to start the meal (my personal favorite).

◇ Each state two things positive about your day and two things negative.

◇ Take turns bringing something to the table to share (like a photo, an item, or a piece of music).

◇ Share proud moments—of yourself or of someone else—with each other.

◇ Create a box, bowl, or other container for writing conversation topics throughout the day or week, then choose from this container during dinner.

◇ Create a "treasure bowl" for placing things to share as you collect them during the day, week, or month.

◇ Have a night per week with a predictable menu—but create fun variations as a family (examples include pizza or grilled cheese sandwiches that can simply be cut in new ways, or you can add new mellow to crazy ingredients).

Resources

When I first started in the autism field, there were very few resources available on the subject. I remember looking for simple mentions in my textbooks about autism and getting excited when I found them. Now there are more books, articles, websites, and organizations specifically for, with, about, and by autistic individuals and their families than one could even attempt to read. I do have my favorites, many referenced in this book, that I share with you here. There are and will be more. If you do not find what you are looking for, contact me. You can email me, if you'd like: barbara@synergyautismcenter.com

Websites for Autistic Adults

Jonathan Chase: https://www.jonathanchase.net/

John Elder Robison: http://jerobison.blogspot.com/p/about-john-elder-robison.html

Temple Grandin: http://www.templegrandin.com/

Stephen Shore: https://www.autismasperger.net/

Alex Plank: http://www.alexplank.com/ and https://wrongplanet.net/

Niko Boskovic: https://www.ocdd.org/nikos-blog/

Stephen Wilshire: https://www.stephenwiltshire.co.uk/

Asperger's Experts: https://www.aspergerexperts.com/

Emma's Hope Book: https://emmashopebook.com/category/unreliable-speaker/

Greta Thunberg's mission: https://fridaysforfuture.org/

Naoki Higashida: https://www.wretchesandjabberers.org/bios/naoki-higashida/

The Asperger Experts: https://www.aspergerexperts.com/

Xavier DeGroat Autism Foundation: https://www.xavierdegroatfoundation.org/

General Websites

Spectrum News/INSAR: https://www.spectrumnews.org/

The Autism Society of America: https://www.autism-society.org/

National Autistic Society: https://www.autism.org.uk/

National Institute of Health: https://www.nichd.nih.gov/

Interpersonal Neurobiology: https://www.drdansiegel.com/about/interpersonal_neurobiology/

Interventions and Information

Center for Disease Control and Prevention (site describes several treatments): https://www.cdc.gov/ncbddd/autism/treatment.html

Relationship Development Intervention: www.https://rdiconnect.com/

Center for Connection: https://www.thecenterforconnection.org/

SCERTS® Model: http://scerts.com/

Applied Behavior Analysis (ABA): https://www.abadegreeprograms.net/faq/what-is-applied-behavior-analysis-in-simple-terms/

TEACCH® Autism Program: https://teacch.com/

DIR/FloorTime: https://www.icdl.com/dir

The Hanen Centre®: http://www.hanen.org/

Early Start Denver Model (ESDM): https://www.esdm.co/

Pivotal Response Treatment: https://education.ucsb.edu/autism/pivotal-response-treatment

Video Modeling: http://www.watchmelearn.com/video -modeling/what-is-video-modeling

Rapid Prompting Method: https://www.halo-soma.org/

Growing Kids Therapy Center: https://growingkidstherapy.com/

Social Stories: https://carolgraysocialstories.com/

Social Thinking: https://www.socialthinking.com/

Center for AAC and Autism: https://www.aacandautism.com/

PreK Teach and Play: https://prekteachandplay.com/

Collaborative Problem Solving–Dr. Ross Greene's work: https://drrossgreene.com/

Think:Kids—Rethinking Challenging Kids: https://thinkkids.org/

Self-Reg—Stuart Shanker: www.self-reg.ca

Polyvagal Theory—Stephen Porges: https://www.stephenporges.com/

For Further Inquiry

DSM-5 (Diagnostic and Statistical Manual 5): https://dsm.psychiatryonline.org/

Autism Diagnostic Criteria: https://www.cdc.gov/ncbddd /autism/hcp-dsm.html

Parent-Mediated Intervention: https://www.nichd.nih .gov/health/topics/autism/conditioninfo/treatments/ parent-mediated

"The Spoon Theory" by Christine Miserandino: https://www .youtube.com/watch?v=jn5IBsm49Rk

"Mindsight and Integration" by Dr. Daniel Siegel: https://www .youtube.com/watch?v=0TK62FdzzTs

Window of Tolerance: https://www.attachment-and-trauma -treatment-centre-for-healing.com/blogs/understanding-and -working-with-the-window-of-tolerance

Trauma-Informed Care: https://www.nctsn.org/trauma -informed-care

Vygotsky's Zone of Proximal Development: https://www .simplypsychology.org/Zone-of-Proximal-Development.html

The Gottman Institute: https://www.gottman.com/

Brené Brown's 50/50 Myth: https://brenebrown.com/podcast /brene-on-comparative-suffering-the-50-50-myth-and-settling -the-ball/

Negative Effects of Long-Term Stress: https://www.nichd.nih.gov/newsroom/releases/stress

Taming the Fight-or-Flight Response: https://www.verywellmind.com/taming-the-fight-or-flight-response-378676

Harvard's Serve and Return Concept: https://developingchild.harvard.edu/science/key-concepts/serve-and-return/

Spoon Theory: https://outline.com/F5xh5V

The 5-Point Scale: https://www.5pointscale.com/

Wretches and Jabberers movie: https://www.wretchesandjabberers.org/

Auditory Processing and Autism: https://www.sciencedirect.com/science/article/abs/pii/S0149763411002065

Pathological Demand Avoidance: https://www.pdasociety.org.uk/

ADDitude—Inside the ADHD mind: https://www.additudemag.com/

Families of Adults Affected by Asperger's Syndrome: http://www.faaas.org/

Imagine—David Pitonyak's work: http://dimagine.com/

Autism Discussion Page: https://www.facebook.com /autismdiscussionpage/

The Ultimate Chore List (by age): https://childdevelopmentinfo .com/chores/the-ultimate-list-of-age-appropriate-chores/#gs. exlmw9

Mona Delahooke's work: https://monadelahooke.com/

Researchers

Beatrice Beebe: https://www.beatricebeebe.com/

Ami Klin: https://www.sfari.org/team/ami-klin/

Alan Sroufe: https://www.researchgate.net/profile/L _Alan_Sroufe

Barbara Rogoff: https://people.ucsc.edu/~brogoff/

Alan Fogel: https://utah.academia.edu/AlanFogel

Laura Cirelli: https://pubmed.ncbi.nlm.nih.gov/?term =Cirelli+LK&cauthor_id=28830004

Connie Kasari: http://www.kasarilab.org/

Stephen Porges: https://kinseyinstitute.org/about/profiles
/sporges.php

Michael Tomasello: https://psychandneuro.duke.edu/people
/michael-tomasello

Peter Hobson: https://thepsychologist.bps.org.uk/volume-29
/september/i-have-been-fortunate-my-professional-life and
https://iris.ucl.ac.uk/iris/browse/profile?upi=RPHOB00

Edward Tronick: https://www.umb.edu/academics/cla
/faculty/edward_tronick

Books

From Surviving to Thriving by Jonathan Chase: https://www
.jonathanchase.net/

The Yes Brain, The Whole-Brain Child, No-Drama Discipline,
and *The Power of Showing Up* by Dr. Daniel Siegel, MD, and Dr.
Tina Payne-Bryson, Ph.D.: https://www.tinabryson.com/books

Parenting from the Inside Out by Dr. Daniel Siegel, MD, and
Mary Hartzell, MEd: https://www.drdansiegel.com/books
/parenting_from_the_inside_out/

Uniquely Human by Barry M. Prizant, Ph.D., with Tom Fields-
Meyer: https://barryprizant.com/uniquely-human/

Brain-Based Parenting by Daniel A. Hughes and Jonathan Baylin: https://www.psychologytoday.com/us/blog/moral -landscapes/201912/brain-based-parenting-understand-and -heal-the-parent-brain

The Autistic Brain and *The Loving Push* by Temple Grandin: http://www.templegrandin.com/

Becoming Human: A Theory of Ontogeny and A Natural History of Human Thinking by Michael Tomasello: https:// psychandneuro.duke.edu/people/michael-tomasello

Social and Emotional Development in Early Intervention and *Beyond Behaviors* by Mona Delahooke: https://monadelahooke .com/

Self-Reg and *Reframed* by Stuart Shankar: https://self-reg.ca/

The Neuroscience of Human Relationships by Louis Cozolino: https://wwnorton.com/books/9780393707823

10 Mindful Minutes by Goldie Hawn: https://www.goodreads .com/book/show/10933486-10-mindful-minutes

Hey Warrior by Karen Young: https://www.heysigmund.com /products/hey-warrior/

Selected Bibliography

Alter, Charlotte, Suyin Hayes, and Justin Worland. 2019. "*Time* Person of the Year: Greta Thunberg." *Time*, December 11, 2019. https://time.com/person-of-the-year-2019-greta-thunberg/

Alvarez, Amanda. 2019. "Brain Clock Ticks Differently in Autism." *Medical Express,* February 13, 2019. https://medicalxpress.com/news/2019-02-brain-clock-differently-autism.html

Centers for Disease Control and Prevention. "Spotlight On: Delay between First Concern to Accessing Services." CDC.gov. Last reviewed: August 27, 2019. https://www.cdc.gov/ncbddd/autism/addm-community-report/delay-to-accessing-services.html

Chang, Yah-Chih, Wendy Shih, Rebecca Landa, Ann Kaiser, Connie Kasari. 2018. "Symbolic Play in School-Aged Minimally Verbal Children with Autism Spectrum Disorder." *Journal of Autism Developmental Disorders*. 48 (May):1436–1445. https://doi.org/10.1007/s10803-017-3388-6

Cirelli, Laura K. "How Interpersonal Synchrony Facilitates Early Prosocial Behavior." *Current Opinion in Psychology*, vol. 20, April 2018, pp. 35–39. http://dx.doi.org/10.1016/j.copsyc.2017.08.009

Cuadros Zamara, Esteban Hurtado, Carlos Cornejo. 2020. "Infant-Adult Synchrony in Spontaneous and Nonspontaneous Interactions." *PLoS ONE.* 15 (December): e0244138. https://doi.org/10.1371/journal.pone.0244138

Dell'Amore, Christine. 2011."Heart Can Sync with a Loved One's." *National Geographic News*, May 6, 2011. https://www.nationalgeographic.com/news/2011/5/110504-fire-walking-hearts-beat-science-health-heartbeats/#close

Donnellan, Anne M., David A. Hill, and Martha R. Leary. 2012. "Rethinking Autism: Implications of Sensory and Movement Differences for Understanding and Support." *Frontiers in Integrative Neuroscience* 6 (2012): 124–124. https://doi.org/10.3389/fnint.2012.00124

Elfer, Emily. 2021."Man with Autism Makes History as White House Intern." *Autism Parenting Magazine.* April 7, 2021. https://www.autismparentingmagazine.com/autism-man-white-house-intern/

Fogel, Alan, and Andrea Garvey. 2007. "Alive Communication." *Infant Behavior and Development* 30 (2): 251–257. https://doi.org/10.1016/j.infbeh.2007.02.007

Franchini, Martina, Vickie L. Armstrong, Marie Schaer, and Isabel M. Smith. 2019. "Initiation of Joint Attention and Related Visual Attention Processes in Infants with Autism Spectrum Disorder: Literature Review." *Child Neuropsychology* 25 (3): 287–317. doi:10.1080/09297049.2018.1490706.

Fuertes, Marina, Pedro Lopez dos Santos, Marjorie Beeghly, and Edward Tronick. 2007. "More Than Maternal Sensitivity Shapes Attachment: Infant Coping and Temperament." *Annals of the New York Academy of Sciences* 1094 (1): 292–96. https://doi.org/10.1196/annals.1376.037

Grandin, Temple. 1992. "An Inside View of Autism." In *High-Functioning Individuals with Autism*, edited by Eric Schopler and Gary B. Mesibov, 105–126. https://doi.org/10.1007/978-1-4899-2456-8_6

Hong, Yoo Rha, MD, and Jae Sun Park, MD. 2012. "Impact of Attachment, Temperament, and Parenting on Human Development." *Korean Journal of Pediatrics* 55, (December): 449–454. http://dx.doi.org/10.3345/kjp.2012.55.12.449

Jahromi, Laudan B., Crystal I. Bryce, and Jodi Swanson. 2013. "The Importance of Self-regulation for the School and Peer Engagement of Children with High-functioning Autism." *Research in Autism Spectrum Disorders* 7 (February): 235–246. https://dx.doi.org/10.1016/j.rasd.2012.08.012

Jones, Warren, Ami Klin. 2013. "Attention to Eyes Is Present but in Decline in Two 6-Month-Old Infants Later Diagnosed with Autism." *Nature* 504 (7480):427–31. https://doi.org/10.1038/nature12715

Kaufman-Balamuth, Limor, Beatrice Beebe, Joseph Jaffe, Stanley Feldstein, and Cynthia Crown. 1998. "Four-Month Mother-Infant Gaze Contingencies Predict One-Year Infant Attachment." *Infant Behavior and Development* 21 (April): 499. https://doi.org/10.1016/S0163-6383(98)91712-X

Kaye, Kenneth, and Alan Fogel. 1980. "The Temporal Structure of Face-to-Face Communication between Mothers and Infants." *Developmental Psychology* 16 (5): 454–64. doi:10.1037/0012-1649.16.5.454.

Kennedy Krieger Institute. "Center for Neurodevelopmental Imaging and Research: Motor Skill Learning in Autism." Accessed March 5, 2019. https://www.kennedykrieger. org /research/centers-labs-cores/center-for-neurodevelopmental -and-imaging-research/research-projects/motor-skill-learning -in-autism

Leclère, Chloë, Sylvie Viaux, Marie Avril, Catherine Achard, Mohamed Chetouani, Sylvain Missonnier, and David Cohen. 2014. "Why Synchrony Matters During Mother-Child Interactions: A Systematic Review." *PLoS ONE* 9 (December): e113571. https://doi.org/10.1371/journal.pone.0113571

Mundy, Peter, Marian Sigman, and Connie Kassari. 1990. "A Longitudinal Study of Joint Attention and Language Disorders in Autistic Children." *Journal of Autism and Developmental Disorders* 20 (March): 115–128. https://doi.org/10.1007 /BF02206861

Paparella, Tanya, and Stephanny F.N. Freeman. 2015. "Methods to Improve Joint Attention in Young Children with Autism: A Review." *Pediatric Health, Medicine, and Therapeutics* 6 (5): 65–78. https://doi.org/10.2147/PHMT.S41921

Reber, Deborah. "The Power of Mirror Neurons and Why Parents' Energy Matters." *Attitude*. Accessed January 20, 2021. https://www.additudemag.com/calm-down-your-adhd-teen/

Rees, Corinne. 2007. "Childhood Attachment." *British Journal of General Practice* 57(544):920-922 doi:10.3399/096016407782317955

Renner, Britta. 2006. "Curiosity About People: The Development of a Social Curiosity Measure in Adults." *Journal of Personality Assessment* 87 (3): 305–316. doi:10.1207/s15327752jpa8703_11.

Shultz, Sarah, Ami Klin, and Warren Jones. 2018. "Neonatal Transitions in Social Behavior and Their Implications for Autism." *Trends in Cognitive Science* 22 (May): 452–469. https://doi.org/10.1016/j.tics.2018.02.012

Siegel, Daniel J., and Mary Hartzell. 2018. *Parenting From the Inside Out: How a Deeper Self-Understanding can Help You Raise Children Who Thrive*. Brunswick, Victoria: Scribe Publications.

Siegel, Daniel J., and Tina Payne Bryson. 2019. *The Yes Brain: How to Cultivate Courage, Curiosity, and Resilience in Your Child*. New York: Bantam.

———. 2015. *The Whole-Brain Child Workbook: Practical Exercises, Worksheets and Activities to Nurture Developing Minds*. Eau Claire, WI: PESI Publishing & Media.

———. 2015. *No-Drama Discipline*. Melbourne: Scribe Publications.

———. 2021. *The Power of Showing Up: How Parental Presence Shapes Who Our Kids Become and How Their Brains Get Wired*. New York: Ballantine Books.

Stanborough, Rebecca Joy. "Signs of Autism in Babies: A Simple Guide to Developmental Differences." *Healthline*. Accessed March 19, 2021. https://www.healthline.com/health/autism/signs-of-autism-in-babies#bottom-line

Tenuta, Flavinia, Roberto Marcone, Maria Giuseppina Bartolo, Mariarosa Persampieri, and Angela Costabile. 2017."I Look, You Smile: The First Mother–Child Communicative Interaction: A Longitudinal Study." *SAGE Open*, 7(2), 215824401770671. https://doi.org/10.1177/2158244017706715

Acknowledgments

First and foremost, I wish to thank the individuals with autism and their families with whom I have been blessed to know and from whom I have learned so much. Many of you may be reading this book and will recognize some of your stories. I am humbled by your willingness to open up to me through the years. Writing this book has taken me down memory lane with all the wonderful people I have known and adore who are living with autism. Thank you for your trust and your friendship.

I thank my son, Graham, who has lived and grown with my obsession with autism. While he is technically an only child, he has grown up alongside so many of my clients. The autism community has provided additional family members in so many ways. He is an amazing and inspiring young man who continues to keep me on my toes even as he explores his own new adulthood.

I am incredibly grateful for my parents and aunt. They have held me up, guided me to follow my passion of working with individuals with autism, and believed in me even when I haven't believed in myself. Neither this book nor my career would have been possible without them.

Next, I am eternally thankful for my good friend and colleague Jonathan Chase, who is one of my biggest cheerleaders in the field of autism. He has listened to my ups and downs, helped me say no when I would have volunteered too much of my time, and motivated me on a daily basis to write this book.

I thank my writing coach, Kristen Hall-Geisler, who I met through Jonathan Chase and who coached me through the first months of writing then into the nitty-gritty of it all. She has been exactly what I needed to bring this book to fruition. She kept me accountable while encouraging my voice to flow out in written words. She made me feel that what I have to say is important and worth sharing.

And finally, thank you to my amazing girlfriends who have inspired me and kept me whole through thick and thin. I am listing them in the order in which I met these wonderful women: Christine Skinner-Grim, Kristie Pretti-Frontczak, Elizabeth LaCroix, Stephanie Gorman, Debbie Gobel, Mindy Baldwin, Joyce Bernheim, Gretchen Hart, Corinna Gilligan, Lisa Lieberman, Peggy Piers, Ali Grimshaw, Pam Smith, and Monica Pass. Thank you for your belief in me. You have held me up more than you probably could ever know.

Barbara R. Avila, M.S., is a family and community autism specialist, coach, and trainer. A graduate of the University of California, Santa Cruz, and the University of Oregon, Barbara provides both online and in-person training for teams on autism and behavior. She consults with individuals, families, and teams across the globe and across disciplines. While her day-to-day support is to individuals, parents, siblings, grand-parents, teachers, and counselors, she has guided teams in group homes, hospitals, clinics, schools, juvenile detention pro-grams, corrections facilities, law practices, therapy clinics, early intervention programs, and more. She has been in the field for over thirty years and specializes in complex situations involving severely challenging behaviors, custody disputes, and multi-ple agencies, as well as more straightforward scenarios. She has experience working with the full spectrum of autism, from very articulate adults with advanced degrees to those needing alternative modes of communication to share their thinking.

She has worked with individuals with co-occurring disorders that range from depression and anxiety to schizophrenia and suicidality. While she works anywhere in the world, she calls the beautiful Northwest her home. She is an avid lover of dogs, hikes, and the forest in which she lives. While her passion is autism, her bursting pride is for her son who now lives in New York City and studies music.

Also available from Barbara R. Avila, M.S.

Please visit Barbara's website at www.synergyautismcenter.com where she has blog posts, videos, and more information available to you.

She also has a podcast, *Synergy Autism Podcast*, which you might enjoy anywhere you find your podcasts.